ROADMAPPING EMERGENT TECHNOLOGIES

David Tolfree and Alan Smith

ROADMAPPING EMERGENT TECHNOLOGIES

Matador
9 De Montfort Mews
Leicester LE1 7FW, UK
Tel: (+44) 116 255 9311 / 9312
Email: books@troubador.co.uk
Web: www.troubador.co.uk/matador

ISBN 978-1848760-998

A Cataloguing-in-Publication (CIP) catalogue record for this book
is available from the British Library.

Typeset in 11pt Book Antiqua by Troubador Publishing Ltd, Leicester, UK
Printed by TJ International Ltd, Padstow, Cornwall

Matador is an imprint of Troubador Publishing Ltd

CONTENTS

PREFACE

In the first decade of the twenty-first century, we are seeing the outcomes from the advances made by science and technology in the last century. The emergence and progress of the global economy is based on rapid developments in transport, telecommunications and computer technology. The global economy presents unparalleled opportunities for all nations. It promotes international trade and peace by increasing mutual dependence, opens up markets for goods and services for undeveloped countries and forces up competition thus furthering economic development and wealth creation.

The global economy is growing at such a rate that planners and investors increasingly require more sophisticated methods of assessing future trends and markets. At the same time they have to be more aware of the innovations that drive technological developments.

Planning for the future is becoming increasingly difficult for those charged with making the right investment decisions for their companies to succeed or, in the case of governments, for the success of their policies. Governments support infrastructure and basic research programmes. Companies, particularly large ones, create employment, populate industries and generate wealth. The wealth is obtained from the commercial exploitation of a company's intellectual property and its skill base. At all levels, decision-makers are faced with having to make strategic choices that will produce positive outcomes for their companies. The goals are different for Governments but the needs are the same.

Planners use a variety of forecasting methods. Many are based on extrapolations from past patterns on the assumption that these will continue in the future. Qualitative data collected from surveys is analysed and then used to modify predictions. Known as predictive planning, this method is in common use. Trends are expressed in terms of percentage growth or decline.

Innovation is a technology driver and can alter or modify a predicted path. Planners must always be aware of technological trends. Having detailed knowledge of a particular field or an industry is an essential part of the process. For example, the progression of the electronic valve to the transistor then to the microchip, thus advancing telecommunications and computer technology, were only predictable by those with knowledge of developments in the electronics industry. Computer modeling is now used throughout business and industry to produce alternative scenarios by using existing data and changing parameters. It has become a main stream technique and used in areas as diverse as marketing and weather forecasting. This gives the planner choices but there is still a need to have specialist knowledge before a strategic decision can be made.

Delphi, a commonly used technique, makes use of expert judgment based on data derived from questionnaires and feedback from focused groups. This has been employed for many years by government bodies as a means of formulating their future policies in specific areas of technology. In the 1990s, the UK's Foresight Science and Technology Programme was designed from the results of national Delphi surveys.

Whatever methods are adopted, decision makers and planners often require a broader approach on which to make strategic decisions. These do require the use of data gathering and analytical methodologies but must also be based on well-informed expert judgment. All of this information can be incorporated into one comprehensive document called a 'Roadmap'.

Roadmaps are now an established instruments for designing future policies and strategies. They provide an operational approach to help organizations chart where they are going and how they are going to get there. Analogous to geographic roadmaps, they show the starting point and help delineate the best path to take to meet the objectives of the strategic plan.

In Chapters 1 and 2 we introduce technology roadmapping with examples of specific national and international roadmaps. We show how they can be used and the methods employed to gather and analyse data. Chapters 3-9 are devoted to roadmaps in specific application areas related to materials and chemicals, medicine and health, transport, construction, electronics, energy and the environment, and consumer products. In Chapter 10 we examine how roadmapping can be used to assess trends and pathways for the future. We make some predictions about the future by extrapolating from developments in the key emergent technology areas.

In researching material for this book, information has been taken from a variety of sources. Much use has been made of the Internet where many roadmaps are published. Where appropriate, extracts and references have been taken from these roadmaps to show the reader the nature of the roadmaps and how the data and information they provide can give a visualisation of the future. This book is specifically devoted to roadmaps in the emergent technologies since these are having, and will continue to have, the greatest impact on society in the foreseeable future. For example, micro-nanotechnologies can be disruptive technologies and so create new market-product paradigms that facilitate rapid change. They attract risks to those unaware of the market opportunities brought about by such technologies. The rapid development of ink-jet printing that revolutionised the printing equipment industry, with the consequent affect on digital photography and the use of home computers, is one of the best known examples of a disruptive technology in action.

This book collates information about technology roadmaps to give the reader an appreciation of the rapid growth in technological applications and markets. It has not been possible to cover every application area and capture every roadmap. Indeed, many are not published and remain confidential to their owners. They represent part of the owner's intellectual property and investment portfolio since making the right decision at the right time can give real competitive advantage to a company.

While it is hoped that the book will be of general interest, we expect it to be of special value to those charged with making strategic planning decisions in Government, business and industry. More than ever before, such decisions will have a profound impact on the economic and social development of society and even the very future of the planet. Climate change, sustainable energy supply, the cure and prevention of disease, satisfying the demand for health care, pose unprecedented challenges for society since they underpin economic development. These are global issues that require people, nations and regions to come together to agree on how the emerging technologies can provide acceptable solutions to the problems that face the world in the coming decades.

The authors wish to thank the many professionals whose work we have referenced, some of whom we have had the pleasure to work with on a variety of projects. In particular, Professor Steven Walsh, who provided a Forward to this book and raised the interest in technology roadmapping to one of us whilst working on the first International Roadmap on Microtechnologies. We would also like to acknowledge the proof reading skills of Valerie Tolfree, the wife of one of the authors, whose encouragement and patience helped in the preparation of this book.

David Tolfree
Alan Smith

FORWARD

David Tolfree and Alan Smith have put together a truly exceptional book on Technology Roadmapping. It provides the reader with ten chapters that cover all aspects of roadmapping from the methodology to actual examples taken from roadmaps in most of the key areas.

Roadmapping has developed over the last 20 years as decision-makers in companies and Governments seek to decrease risk of applying new technology but at the same time realising the benefits it can bring. The pace of technological change is increasing exponentially making it difficult for strategists and decision-makers to fully utilise technology for competitive advantage. Technology roadmapping is now extensively used as a tool to assist in this process. Some roadmaps fail because they are focused more on marketing and less on the technology strategy paradigm. These and other aspects are clearly set out in the first Chapter of the book where the strategic and operational aspects of roadmapping are emphasised.

In the second chapter, the authors provide a set of common roadmapping methodologies and show how these can be used for different situations, depending on whether the study is for a company, an industry sector, a regional or Government programme. In Chapters 3-9, examples and extracts taken from published roadmaps in key sectors such as materials, medicine, transport, electronics and energy are given to provide practitioners with a real insight into how roadmapping is being used for planning the future. In Chapter 10, 'Roadmapping the Future' the reader is taken on a journey from the present into the future showing how roadmapping new developments in technology enable us to make realistic predictions of the shape of things to come. This is graphically illustrated on the book's front cover.

This book is well written and concise, providing readers with invaluable information about how to use roadmapping as tool for strategic planning. Not every roadmap is covered but the examples cited show the wide use of the method. I recommend this book to all professions involved in strategic planning and to students and others who want to learn more about the technique.

Steve Walsh
Alfred Black Professor of Entrepreneurship,
University of New Mexico Anderson School of Management.

Dr. Walsh is one of the world's leading experts on the commercialization of micro and nano technologies. He is the founding President of MANCEF and Co-chair of the first ever-technological roadmap for MEMS and Top Down Nano technologies.

ABOUT THE AUTHORS

David Tolfree MSc., F.Inst.P., CPhys., F.IoN. was the co-founder and Executive Director of Technopreneur Ltd, a consultancy company for the exploitation of micro-nanotechnology, established at Daresbury in Cheshire, England. He is one of the founders of MANCEF (Micro and Nanotechnology Commercialization Educational Foundation), an international body dedicated to commercialization and education, and is currently its European Vice President. David is also one of the founders of the UK Institute of Nanotechnology and is a member of its Advisory Board. He is a Chartered Physicist, a Fellow of the Institute of Physics and the Institute of Nanotechnology and has published over 140 papers, including news articles, chapters for books and conference papers, and has given interviews on television and radio. He has co-authored chapters in the MANCEF International Microsystems and Top-Down Nanotechnology Roadmap. He is the co-editor and writer of a book published in October 2007. *Commercialising Micro-Nanotechnology Products*. This was the first book dedicated to the subject of commercialization to be published.

David gained over 40 years' experience in research, project management and the marketing of research facilities while employed by the Council for the Central Laboratory of the Research Councils (CCLRC) at Daresbury in the UK. His earlier career was spent doing basic research in nuclear particle and accelerator physics, reactor instrumentation, and nuclear weapons development. In 1994, whilst working at the Daresbury Laboratory, he was the first to establish non-silicon microfabrication technology in the UK, transferring much of it from Germany. At that time he was appointed to be the UK coordinator of the first European R&D Network in Microtechnology involving nine countries. He established the first industry-led UK network in LIGA technology, known as the LIGA Club, and acquired over £500K of funding for prototype microstructure development using deep X-ray lithography. Afterwards, he created the SMIDGEN (Small Microengineering Intelligence Design Generation Exploitation Network), a consortium of companies and universities, to drive the commercial exploitation of microsystems technologies. Acknowledged by the UK Government's Foresight Directorate as an example of best practice, it laid the early foundations to the UK MNT Network, part of Government's £92 million Micro and Nanotechnology Manufacturing Initiative (2003-2007). David contributed to the network's programme to engage industry and academia using a roadmapping technique to form specialist technology focused groups.

David has contributed to MANCEF's International Commercialisation of Microsystems Conferences (COMS) since 1994, as a Co-Director, Chair, and Speaker. He is a Co-Director of the COMS2009 conference in Denmark in 2009. He is currently Co-Chair of the International HARMST-LIGA Commercialization Group.

David's interests are writing, film-making, photography, promoting science and technology to the public, including schools and colleges, swimming and gardening.

 Dr Alan Smith BSc., PhD., FLS, FRSC., FIMMM is the Managing Director of AZ-TECH consultancy company. His career began in academia as a lecturer, before he moved into industry. He has been a member of the UK Government's Foresight Panels for both Chemistry and Materials, and has served on industrial advisory boards for two universities. He is a Past President of the Industrial Affairs Division of the Royal Society of Chemistry, and is a member of the Bureau of IUPAC. He was Chairman of the COMIT Faraday Partnership, and Board Member of the IMPACT Faraday Partnership. He was a visiting tutor and lecturer on Innovation and R&D Management for an MSc course at a Scottish university.

He has also managed a number of projects for the UK Government and was Associate Director of the MNT Network, a Government initiative on nanotechnology. He is the author of numerous papers on nanotechnology, and he lectures on the subject to schoolchildren and the general public, as well as to international experts. He has recently introduced nanotechnology and roadmapping to heads of State of Commonwealth Countries at a global conference in Africa. In addition, Alan is a consultant on nanotechnology to two major international companies, and is a non-executive director of a UK university spin-out company.

He has facilitated over 50 roadmaps in a variety of sectors, many for UK Government sponsored organisations, as well as for the European Commission, and the Government of the Republic of South Africa. He was awarded the Thornton Medal for 2008 by the Institute of Materials, Minerals and Mining for facilitating roadmaps and giving presentations on nanotechnology.

Alan was co-editor of a book entitled *Trends and Priorities in the UK Chemical Industry* for the Chemical Industries Association, and a co-author of a book entitled *Future Perspectives of European Materials Research*.

CHAPTER 1

INTRODUCTION TO TECHNOLOGY ROADMAPPING

CONTENTS

INTRODUCTION

Now, in the first decade of the twenty-first century, it is apparent that the emergent technologies will play a significant part in shaping the future. Linked to the sciences that produced them, they are already driving the knowledge-based economy by creating the foundations of new industries and the formation of new markets. For example, in areas such as telecommunications, they are responsible for the formation and operation of international networks that connect the world, thus advancing the development of the global economy.

New and potentially disruptive technologies such as nanotechnology, biotechnology, robotics, and artificial intelligence are currently perceived to be some of those that will have the greatest impact. The solutions to many of the world's problems, namely climate change, prevention of disease, environmental pollution and sustainable energy supply will be found by the application of new technologies. If solutions are not found in the near future, global consequences will result. The economic, social and political ramifications will have to be faced by every nation. National interest will give way to actions that will be necessary for the survival of the whole human race.

The Utopian goal of eradicating disease and poverty, prolonging life, producing abundant food and energy, instant communication, fast access to knowledge and raising the standard of living for everyone is now within our grasp. It may take many decades or even centuries to achieve such aspirations but they are no longer in the realms of science fiction. Progress towards achieving these goals is inextricably linked to strategic long-term planning and the utilisation of knowledge and resources.

Technology is the practical application of science through the employment of engineering skills and tools. Only advanced industrial nations have these resources available but very often economic and political considerations restrict their availability. Therefore a degree of strategic planning is required to optimise and rationalise their use. This is part of a process known as 'Roadmapping', a term

2

first coined by Motorola decades ago, but only widely adopted recently by individual companies, industry sectors and governments as a strategic planning tool. A Google search showed at least 100 roadmaps were freely available over the Internet.

Roadmapping provides a strategic and operational approach to help organisations chart where they are going and how they are going to get there. Analogous to geographic roadmaps, they show us our starting point and where we want to go. However, it is the path taken to arrive at our destination that determines the choices we make.

Roadmaps enable the decision-makers in nations, industries, companies and organisations to visualise and plan their assets to meet future goals. They provide the best guidance on which to make strategic decisions. Technology roadmapping integrates science and engineering, the basic disciplines for developing future products and industries. Over many years, hundreds of technology roadmaps have been produced which gives credence to their value. They have become a well-used tool in the chest of the planner. However, not all roadmaps embrace the wider issues facing the world and its population or are easily accessible to all who seek and need the information they contain. We are now approaching a time when accurate planning for the future is more important to civilisation than ever before; human survival may even depend on it.

DEVELOPMENT OF TECHNOLOGY ROADMAPPING

The global market is placing industry under intense pressure to deliver a higher volume of quality goods and services more competitively to a rapidly expanding market. This is currently being driven by the demands of the growing Asian markets that have an insatiable desire for goods and services. Companies who wish to succeed in this market have to face the following challenges.

- Rapid technology change
- High cost and risk of R&D

3

- Stockholder demand for near-term profits
- Increasing government regulation
- Customer pressures on costs
- Increasing technology / product complexity
- Need for environmental acceptability.

During the late eighties and through the nineties cost cutting, down-sizing and re-engineering took place. These short-term measures helped cash flow and increased profits but technological innovation is the only route to long-term sustainable growth and stability.

In the past, 'Foresight' exercises were an excellent way of stimu-lating organisations to think about the future. They helped govern-ments and organisations to plan ahead and determine what was needed. 'Foresight' was more of a vision. It is a process that system-atically attempts to look into the longer-term future of science, tech-nology, the economy, environment and society. Its aim is to identify areas of research and development most likely to yield the greatest economic and social benefits. Foresight programmes can clearly set the scene for the future, but few actually detail how organisations should get there. Roadmapping does not just take a 'forward look'; it also goes through the process of how to get there, fills the gaps and establishes clear goals about how to achieve the objectives. The term 'Roadmapping' has been used for over thirty years, but it is only in the last ten that it has become an established management tool. Almost every industry is covered by the production of at least one type of roadmap.

Different types of roadmaps are required to deal specifically with economic, technological and political issues. In areas like energy conservation, health or environmental change, different types of roadmaps have to be integrated into a single plan, otherwise workable solutions become difficult to achieve. Problems such as identifying alternative energy sources, distributing healthcare or slowing down climate change require multi-dimensional analysis to accommodate the many variables present. Roadmaps have to include such analysis for them to be useful to decision-makers.

4

Technology roadmaps are key elements in the process because unlike strategic plans they often integrate the talents of diverse stakeholders. They help industry, supply-chains, academic and research groups, and governments come together to jointly identify and prioritise support for those technologies that will produce results better aligned to business goals.

Technology roadmapping is driven by a need, not a solution. For example, if the need exists for energy efficient transport systems to achieve low mileage costs per gallon then the incorporation of lightweight composite materials into the vehicles is a possible solution. However, there may be other more appropriate solutions such as improved engine control and management, or even a more efficient fuel. Therefore, the need is the starting point, not a pre-defined solution.

Technology roadmaps look at the trends and drivers facing a particular topic, and the time horizons in which they are likely to be important. By linking market opportunities to product and technology developments, roadmaps can help support the communication of technology strategies and plans by:

- REDUCING technology investment risk
- IDENTIFYING market opportunities
- IMPROVING competitiveness
- IDENTIFYING the critical technologies and core competencies needed
- INVOLVING supply chains in the planning process.

The roadmapping process only started to gain wide scale use during the last decade. Initially a high proportion of the technology roadmaps originated in North America which has a more established business culture. However, in recent years other regions and countries have added to the increasing volume of material available. For example, the European Union (EU) now uses the roadmapping tool in many of its Technology Platform Programmes.

Technology roadmapping provides a way to identify, evaluate, and select technology alternatives that can be used to satisfy need. However, it is only a high-level strategy for developing these technologies. A more detailed plan is then often required to specify the actual projects and activities. This is simply traditional project management, not something unique to technology roadmapping.

A technology roadmap can identify alternate technology paths for meeting certain criteria and mission objectives. A single path may be selected and a plan developed. If there is high uncertainty or risk, then multiple paths may be selected and pursued concurrently. Some organisations have effectively combined the characteristics of both types of technology roadmaps. Both should be integrated with other business planning techniques.

Roadmaps for the emergent technologies, the principal subject of this book, have a very special role in the strategic planning process because they generally refer to disruptive technologies (1). A disruptive technology is used to create a product, or service that eventually overturns the existing dominant technology or existing product in the market. Sometimes a disruptive technology comes to dominate an existing market by filling a role in a new market that the older technology could not fill. Schumpeter calls them 'creative destroyers' (2). By his definition, such innovations are so radical that they destroy existing markets and the dominant companies that supply these markets, replacing them with entirely new markets and companies who use new technologies. Recent examples are digital cameras with optical microchips replacing film and ink-jet printing replacing typewriters.

It is vital for companies, governments, and nations to be aware of the implications of disruptive technologies due to their impact on future economies. Multi-billion dollar industries can be transformed or even extinguished in a very short time with disastrous consequences if plans are not in place to deal with those consequences. However, companies who have the knowledge and have done their roadmapping, can exploit such technologies and become commercially successful, even market leaders, in a very short time.

Emergent technologies can put all industries under threat if they are not prepared. This raises the importance of roadmapping as a forecasting technique for strategic planners and places greater emphasis on how data should be collected and analysed. These roadmaps must be scoped to include the economic and social consequences of planning decisions since the industrial and service sectors are the major employers. The methods employed to acquire data and information and the sources used, relate to its quality. These methods will be discussed extensively in Chapter 2 of this book.

Nanotechnology, one of the key emerging technologies, has the potential to be disruptive. Like microtechnology, that was responsible for the revolution in printing and computing, nanotechnology will have an even greater impact in the development of new materials. In the future these will revolutionise almost every manufacturing sector.

Roadmapping nanotechnology poses a number of problems since, unlike sustaining technology-based roadmaps, nanotechnologies are not well-defined. They can be applied to distinctly different processes, top-down or bottom-up. The explanations of these terms which is well documented in the literature (3) and can be summarised as follows: in the 'bottom-up' approach, materials and devices are built from molecular components which assemble themselves chemically by principles of molecular recognition. In the 'top-down' approach, nano-objects are constructed from larger entities without atomic-level control. Both of these approaches are moving towards the same ultimate outcome, *atomically precise manufacturing*. The roadmapping of processes, products and markets therefore requires a different set of paradigms from those used for other disruptive technologies, such as microtechnologies or microsystems where unit cells like transistors and silicon chips exist. However, in nanotechnology there is no physical single unit cell as a component. This distinguishes nanotechnology from other tehcnologies.

Forecasting the development and commercialisation of a new or emerging technology can place companies and even nations in a competitive position in the global market, but to sustain that position also requires foresight on how the technology, its products and

7

markets, will continue to develop. Product manufacture requires the use and application of many technologies. Having a unique advance in materials may require a new process for manufacturing products from them. For example, the development of ink-jet printing using microfluidics nozzle technology required special inks that would flow and mix at the micro level before they could replace conventional printing methods. Digital photography required new, cheap high resolution optical arrays and microchip processors before they could match the quality of high grain film. This has now been largely achieved with obvious supplier and customer benefits. The new technologies will give rise to many more innovative developments and products.

The above are examples where a disruptive technology did rely on other factors, such as the need to satisfy public appetite for low cost innovative products that give the user a degree of control. It was also the availability of low cost home computers that made processing of images from digital cameras possible, thus greatly extending the domestic market demand for ink-jet printers and digital cameras. Roadmaps would have predicted the timing and market possibilities of such innovations, and therefore manufacturers and suppliers who were prepared had a significant competitive advantage over those who did not have the information to invest in the necessary production facilities.

TYPES OF TECHNOLOGY ROADMAPS

There are basically three different types of roadmaps, as illustrated in Figure 1.1.

Industry Sector Roadmaps
The first types of roadmaps are for major industry sectors such as chemicals, pharmaceuticals, automotive and aerospace, medical and health etc. Inevitably these required a large number of people for their production; but their importance in helping decision makers in

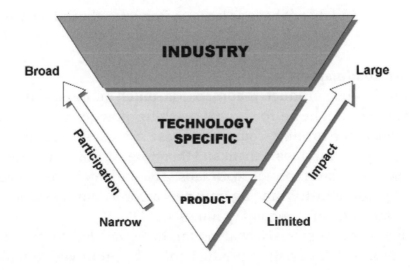

Figure 1.1

companies who work in the sectors can be judged by their success in the market.

Technology Specific Roadmaps
Some examples of the second types which are technology specific are:

- Nanomaterials and the Chemical Industry
- Bio-catalysis
- Alumina technology
- Alternative media, conditions and raw materials
- Materials of construction, operation in the Chemical Process Industries
- New process chemistry
- Colloid and interface science
- Nanocomposites
- Tissue engineering.

These roadmaps tend to be less broad in terms of the number of participants and do not have as large an impact as the industry sector ones.

Product Roadmaps

The third type, product roadmaps, is much more specific and, for example, might be for a new washing powder or toothpaste for a consumer product company. These are usually confidential to the company producing them and therefore are not widely distributed like the other types of roadmaps. The authors have facilitated roadmaps for industry, ranging from new aerosol delivery systems, to the manufacture of detergent granules and IT.

One or more process systems might be needed to produce a single product. An existing product could be improved to make it more usable and competitive by employing a new manufacturing process. The production of stain-proof clothes using a new nanocoating technique is one example of innovation in processing made possible by applying hybrid polymer nano-layers on cloth fibres; although this is not exactly within the strict defintion of a disruptive technology paradigm as it compliments an existing range of products rather than displacing them. Further developments of the process that brings significant material and cost benefits to the mass manufacture of clothing could revolutionise the textile industry. It would then be classified as being disruptive. This is where roadmapping both the process and product technologies would be of great value to the industry. This was acknowledged by the UK Technitex conference (4) in Leeds in 2004.

Company Roadmaps

Roadmaps developed by companies are specifically related to their needs and are often confidential to those who own them.

Sector Roadmaps

Roadmaps produced by industry sectors are usually available from trade associations or published by them and industry groups. These are important as they reveal trends both in products technology and markets.

National Roadmaps

Roadmaps that are funded or supported by governments and their agencies are usually in the public domain and available to review via websites. They specifically relate to key policies in areas like health, transport, energy and communication. National laboratories such as Sandia and Berkeley in the United Sates of America and Knowledge Transfer Networks in the UK are just two of the many that produce technology roadmaps

International Roadmaps

European

A number of European organisations, including the European Commission (EC), have been proactive in producing roadmaps. Planning for the future technological, economic and social development of Europe has always been at the centre of the European Union's treaties. It is therefore not surprising that there is a huge amount of information embedded in the plethora of roadmaps that cover almost every sector. Using published extracts, we have outlined some of these roadmaps below although many of the sectors and topics are described in greater detail in later chapters of this book.

NEXUS Roadmaps

NEXUS (the European Network of Excellence in Multifunctional Microsystems) produced a roadmap from a market analysis on microsystems for the years 2004-2009 (5). This was a follow-up from an earlier study on products and markets in 2003.

The report is essentially a roadmap for future markets. Overall, it concludes that microsystems including sensors and actuators are consolidating their position in established markets and finding new applications. The report indicates that over the next five years, this market is predicted to grow at a rate of 16% per year from $12 billion in 2004 to $25 billion in 2009 across a spectrum of 26 MST/MEMS products. The results of this analysis are summarised in Table 1.1.

Table 1.1: NEXUS Report

	Consumer Electronics	Medical	Communications	Aerospace Defence	Automotive	Other
Inertial Sensors	Pedometer Game control, image stability, hard disc protection	Motion tracking pacemaker		Missile Guidance, navigation, laser range finders	Airbag, vehicle control active suspension systems	Seismic exploration, robotic machines , vibrations
Optical Devices	Microdisplays autofocus lenses	Microspectrometers for patient self testing	Viable optical attenuators, tuneable filters			Micromirrors
RF MEMS			Tuneable capacitors and resonators for mobile phones and base stations	Switches and tuneable capacitors for radar communication		Switches, relays
Microphones	Mobile phones, notebooks camcorders	Hearing Aids			Hands free calling	
Microfluidic Devices	Inkjet heads	Lab on Chip (PoCs), micro needles				Micro dispensing, gas and liquid chromatography, microcooling microreactors
Pressure Sensors	Altimeters	Blood pressure, kidney dialysis		Flight control systems, cabin pressure		
Flow sensors		Lung function			Air intake of engine	
IR sensors	Cabin temperature control, crash prevention	Thermometer Diagnostics		Security monitoring		Home climate . microwave control, ventilation
Others	Fingerprint sensors			Fingerprint sensors for authentication		Probe cards for electrical heating

Microsystems and MEMS (Micro Electromechanical Systems) Applications (5)

It provides an extensive list of applications for microsystems and without considering additional markets that will be affected by nanomaterials and nanostructures. We have summarised below some extracts from the Nexus report on key sectors to illustrate the type of information that is available in such a roadmap. Roadmaps for many of these product sectors will be described in later chapters.

Automotive

Automotive was the first mass market for micro-and nanosystems products and has been the industry driver. The increasing complexity of cars, due to demands on safety, driver and passenger comfort and environmental restrictions will ensure the future growth of this market. Expected growth areas are: IR sensors for air quality, accelerometers and gyroscopes safety and stability, micro scanners for displays, sensors for tyre pressure and engine management etc.

IT Peripherals

The major products, in terms of micro- and nanosystems, within the IT peripherals market are read/write heads and inkjet print heads. Both product categories are under pressure due to alternative technologies offered: respectively by solid-state memories and laser printing. New micro and nanosystems applications in this field include microphones, accelerometers.

Telecommunications

The optical telecom market is expected to grow steadily over the coming years and optical micro and nanosystems will play an important role in this growth. The competition from wireless communication is making this market a difficult one to assess. The wireless market is dependent on the variety of new functionalities on offer by miniaturised RF components.

Medical and Life Science Applications

A paradigm shift is taking place in present healthcare from therapeutic to a preventive medicine. One of the enablers behind this will be microfluidic-based Point-of-Care (PoC) instruments and other, Lab-on-Chip (LoC) devices. The result will be more effective, personalised, safe and cost-effective therapy, better diagnosis and treatment and, most importantly, increased patient satisfaction. The adoption of microfluidics will also significantly reduce the time and cost of producing large amounts of biological material, which helps drug developing companies to reduce initial expenses of drug development. Most diagnostic companies have included microfluidics within their development roadmaps, regarding it as a key enabling technology. Other applications of micro and nanosystems in the medical fields include: accelerometers in pace makers, microphones in hearing aids, microneedles and micropumps for medicine delivery.

Household Applications

Initially micro and nanosystems devices were considered to be too expensive for the household market. Pressure and temperature sensors are the most abundantly found micro and nanosystems devices for household applications, and accelerometers for washing machines are regarded as a growth area.

Industrial Process Control

The reliability, scalability, sensitivity, and cost-effective solutions offered by micro and nanosystems technology have the potential to provide viable sensor solutions for industrial automation. The trend towards micro and nanosystems enabled miniaturisation is certainly strengthened by the increasing interest in miniaturised, remotely powered, autonomous sensor systems. The small size of micro and nanodevices makes them especially suitable in volume-constrained applications; also, the low energy consumption and high precision of these devices are essential for wireless monitoring. Integration is a prerequisite for multi-sensor network applications. With regards to cost, industrial automation is less price-sensitive than the higher volume markets such

14

as that of consumer electronics, but much more demanding in application support and offering total solutions. Applications of interest include: corrosion control, pressure and flow sensing, gas sensors, accelerometers for vibration control and energy harvesting.

Aerospace, Defence and Security

Except for inertial sensors, and possibly, smart munitions, this area is characterised by low volumes, particularly when compared to consumer electronics, automotive and Point-of-Care diagnostics. Development work for these market segments is usually undertaken in conjunction with activities for other market sectors. Many of the products therefore have their analogues in other markets such as pressure sensors, gyros, accelerometers, IR sensors, etc.

Sensors, in general, are used in aircraft for measurement of altitude, direction of navigation, speed, cabin pressure and temperature, fuel quantity as well as for engine and hydraulic management and control. For example, the low cost and low power of electronic integration of micro and nanosensors makes them suitable for distributed measurement which enables more accurate maintenance and control.

Consumers Electronics and Life Style Products

Consumer electronics is a good market area for suppliers of accelerometers, microphones and other micro and nanosystems products. The increasing number of functionalities within smaller and smaller devices promotes the drive to decrease the size of electronic components and subsystems. Apple's iPhone and Nintendo's Wii console are examples of the use of accelerometers for image stabilisation and gaming control. Other applications include: microphones and zoom lenses in mobile phones and oscillators in watches. High-end mobile phones now employ inertial sensors such as accelerometers and gyros for scrolling, character recognition, gaming and image stabilisation.

Market Analysis

The financial breakdown shown in the NEXUS market analysis for

Table 1.2: Market Growth for Sectors

	2004 ($B)	2009 ($B)
IT Peripherals	8.0	13.7
Consumer Electronics	0.8	5.5
Automotive	1.3	2.0
Medical/Life Science	0.6	1.5
Telecommunications	0.2	0.9
Indust Process Control	0.6	0.9
Aero, Defence/Security	0.1	0.4
Household applications	0.1	0.2

the years 2004-2009 given in Table 1.2 provides a clear indication of the scope of the economic sectors that are directly affected by MNT with their current investment trends.

As can be seen, investments are expected to keep on growing so much that market may reach $20 billion in 2010, with a growth rate of around 20% for micro and nanoproducts.

Nanoroadmap (NRM) (6)
This is a project co-funded by the European Commisssion (EC) within The Sixth Framework Programme (FP6) (Thematic Priority 3) whose objective is the production of technology roadmaps about nanotechnology applications in three different sectors within which twelve topics were selected.

An international consortium, consisting of partners coming from eight European countries and Israel was established to carry out the project. Its aim was to carry out a long-term (10 years) forecasting exercise on the application of nanotechnology in the fields of materials, health and medical systems and energy. The outcomes were compiled in 12 roadmaps (4 for each sector).

The European industry, the research organisations (public and private), public bodies within the European countries, the EC, and the financial community, are expected to be the key users of these roadmaps. They will also be used to address future R&D strategies.

Micro-Nanomanufacturing (MINAM)

The 126-page report of the European Micro- and Nanomanufacturing Technology Platform group MINAM (7) is essentially derived from a set of roadmaps of future micro-nanomanufacturing in relation to technology providers, manufacturers and equipment suppliers. MINAM was created to support the European manufacturers and equipment-suppliers in the field of manufacturing micro-and nanotechnology products. The driving forces, business needs and requirements behind the establishment of the MINAM group are defined by the necessity to broaden the range of the microsystems-based products and at the same time to multiply their capabilities by the introduction of new materials and processes which will develop from nanotechnology.

The MINAM Report addresses several key areas: manufacturing of nanomaterials, processing of nanosurfaces, micromanufacturing processes and integrated systems and platforms for micro-and nanomanufacturing. The outlined trends and research and development priorities are illustrated with examples from key industrial sectors in Europe. It examines in detail the future social and economic impact that the technologies will have by linking them to major driving factors such as applications, markets and technological capabilities.

Four of the chapters in the report cover the manufacturing of nanomaterials, manufacturing of nanosurfaces, manufacturing of microcomponents and integrated micro and nanomanufacturing systems and platforms. A later chapter includes contributions from some of the MINAM industrial partners and gives an idea about current applications and expected trends for the upcoming years.

Other International Roadmaps

In recent years some international bodies such as the Micro and Nanotechnology Commercialisation and Education Foundation

(MANCEF) (8) and the Semiconductor Equipment and Materials International (SEMI) (9) have produced definitive roadmaps that embrace both existing and emerging technologies. In the MANCEF International Top-Down Nanotechnology Roadmap produced in 1990 (10), many examples are given of processes that use a mixture of these technologies but are application specific. If we use the term 'small technology' to embrace both micro-nanotechnologies then four separate laws can be used to define the relationship between the variables, application, process, package and test. Walsh et al (11) describes how these laws provide a basis to understand 'small technology' and how it should be treated in a roadmapping process. These roadmaps include contributions from most of the principal industries and input from 300 companies worldwide so provide essentially an update and a forward look for the industries they represent. These are particularly important as they relate to the global market where the future lies for any forward-looking company that wants to succeed. A comprehensive chapter on the issues raised by nanotechnology roadmapping can be found in the book 'Commercialising Micro-Nanotechnology Products' (12).

REFERENCES

1   http://en.wikipedia.org/wiki/Disruptive_Technology, November 2007.
2   Schumpeter , J., *The theory of economic development.* Harvard University Press, 1934), 75.
3   Nanotechnology – (http://en.wikipedia.org/wiki/Nanotechnology)
4   Present Status and Future Potential of Nanotechnologies in the Textile Industry by David Taylor, TechniTex Conference, Leeds, 30th April 2004, (http://www.hollings.mmu.ac.uk)
5   NEXUS III. Total market for 26 MST/MEMS products, 2004-2009 (http://www. enablingmnt.com)
6   NanoRoadmap Project (http://www.nanoroadmap.it)
7   MINAM (http:// www.minamwebportal.eu)
8   MANCEF (http:// www.mancef.org)
9   The International Technology Roadmap for Semiconductors (ITRS) (http:// www.itrs.net)

10 Walsh, S., MANCEF Roadmap 2002, ISBN:0-9727333-0-2
11 Walsh, S., Giasolli, R. and Elders, J. , The second edition of the international Micro-top-down Nanotechnology Roadmap, 674, MANCEF, Naples, Florida, 2004.
12 Commercialising Micro-Nanotechnology Products, edited by Tolfree, D. and Jackson, M., MCRC Press Taylor & Francis.

CHAPTER 2

ROADMAPPING METHODOLOGIES

CONTENTS

BACKGROUND

The methodology for arriving at a roadmap varies. Some simply rely on a Delphi style questionnaire being sent out to as many people that are thought to be interested. Delphi questionnaires are named after the Oracle at Delphi (1) where experts were invited to give their opinions. Nowadays, however, most people have an aversion to questionnaires that often ask what seem to be irrelevant questions, so usually there is a less than 20% response. Inevitably, the experts whose input is most relevant are often too busy to reply.

It is now recognised that it is crucial to engage experts in the particular field under consideration by highlighting the benefits either to them or their establishments (company or university) or their country. Rather than using Delphi style questionnaires, it is more acceptable to hold workshops to target those most knowledgeable in the particular field, and then receive input from other interested parties through putting a draft technology roadmap on a web site.

STRUCTURE OF TYPICAL TECHNOLOGY ROADMAPS

Peeling back the structure of any technology roadmap that has been created so far shows that they all follow a very similar procedure, which can be summarised as shown in Figure 2.1.

The process is quite logical and can follow the normal brainstorming practices used throughout industry.

Where are we now?
The first step is to establish where you are now, i.e. relative to the competition, which might be just at home or throughout the world. This should be backed up with relevant market research. Such an exercise might determine how far you remain behind your competitors, or could identify gaps that might exist in your market areas.

In addition, the trends and drivers for the topic under investiga-

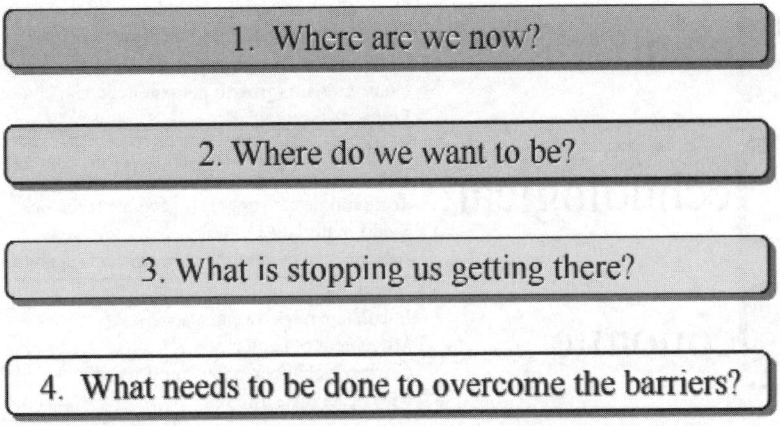

| 1. Where are we now? |
| 2. Where do we want to be? |
| 3. What is stopping us getting there? |
| 4. What needs to be done to overcome the barriers? |

Figure 2.1: The four stages in the roadmapping process

tion need to be highlighted since they will have a major influence on the future direction and technology requirements. As a guideline, it is appropriate to use a STEEP (Social, Technological, Economic, Environmental and Political) process to thoroughly assess the trends and drivers. This uses the 5 steps shown in Figure 2.2 to examine the trends and drivers. This type of process was previously known as a STEP or PEST procedure until the 'Environmental' aspects became more influential.

Where do we want to be?
The second stage is to decide where you want to be in the future; not just short term and medium term but also in the long term. Generally the latter is 10 to 20 years ahead, whereas short term can be up to 2 or 3 years, depending on the sector, and medium term can be up to 10 years. This stage represents the organisation's aspirations both in new products and processes as well as its services. It is also prudent not to put targets down that are totally unrealistic, since that can have a de-motivating effect on all those concerned. Here one has to balance the desire to set goals that will impress the most hardened of CEOs, with targets that are not too outrageous. It seems that governments are

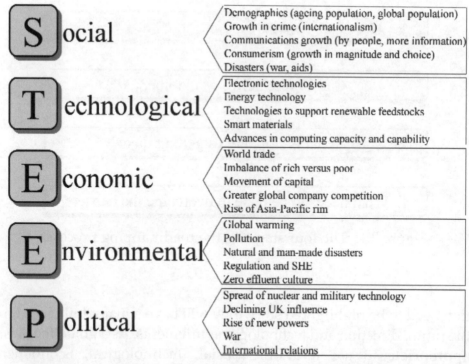

Figure 2.2: STEEP analysis to determine trends and drivers

going through a phase of setting targets that will never be achieved without considerable manipulation of the data.

What is stopping us getting there?

Having set ambitious but realistic targets, the third stage is to ask what are the barriers to getting where we want to be, i.e. what is likely to stop us reaching our goals?

What needs to be done to overcome the barriers?

Finally, it is necessary to say what is needed to overcome those barriers and in what time-scale. This stage is perhaps the most important one to get right, and for a technology roadmap it is likely to be a list of Research and Development priorities, along with timescales.

Sometimes it might be necessary to persuade non-technical leaders that a technology roadmap is going to be a key part of the company's strategy. Some of the key benefits of a roadmap are that it:

- Helps incorporate new technology into the business
- Provides support for a company's strategy and planning
- Identifies new business opportunities
- Provides key information on a business's technological direction
- Improves communication and co-operation within the business
- Identifies technology gaps as well as the market opportunities
- Helps with sourcing decisions, resource allocation, risk management and exploitation decisions
- Provides a common reference or framework through high level integrated planning and control.

Of course, for technical establishments, persuasion should not be needed.

It is most prudent to have people from all aspects of business involved in a technology roadmap exercise since the input from the marketing department is essential and the influence of the manufacturing department is also crucial. Once the technology roadmap has been agreed by all parties, then the R&D programme can be drawn up and the resources (capital investment, supply chain, staffing and skills) allocated.

Specific examples of recent roadmaps

With all the activity going on currently to produce roadmaps and general strategies, the chemical and materials sectors have been particularly prolific. Those available in 2002 were listed in Materials World (2). By way of example, the procedures used for two materials-related roadmaps are summarised below:

Technology Roadmap for Materials of Construction, Operation and Maintenance in the Chemical Process Industry (3)

This technology roadmap was instigated through the US Government's initiative Vision 2020, which was its equivalent of the United Kingdom's Foresight Exercise. The Technology Vision 2020 for the US Chemical Industry had highlighted, in its Materials Technology section, that materials of construction was an important issue, and a decision was made to carry out a detailed investigation of what needed to be done to map out its future requirements in this area.

The "Where are we now?" question was obvious, since most chemical plants are costly and subject to corrosion, as well as being energy intensive. Their first criteria were to set targets upon themselves to illustrate where they wanted to be by 2020. It is worth noting that the targets appear to be quite realistic, which fits well with earlier comments about avoiding setting goals that are clearly unachievable and only de-motivate those charged with achieving them.

In addition, the team of 25 experts detailed the opportunities for industry and their customers' requirements, by carrying out a brainstorming exercise. The thoughts were gathered into related clusters. The most critical problem areas (i.e. where the barriers are) were marked with a priority 'dot'. For a cluster headed "Corrosive Environments" the main priority opportunities for that cluster were drawn out.

Overall the experts were then able to list what they saw as high priority opportunities. Using the same brainstorming procedure the team then set about looking at the barriers to the development of new materials of construction. As before these were grouped into a number of topics, and under these are the lists of barriers, to which priority marks were added. The "Basic Science / Knowledge" cluster for example, prioritised "lack of understanding of materials" as one of the most critical barriers. The final stage was then to set the research needs, and this was carried out in a similar manner. The report shows the results for the near term (0 to 3 years), mid term (3 to 10 years), and the long term (10 to 20 years) research requirements.

In addition to the priorities, an indication was given regarding whether the priorities fell into the following categories: environment, productivity, safety or energy. The team then produced a number of bullet points to indicate the main research priority needs.

Chemical Industry R&D Roadmap in Nanomaterials by Design (4)
The procedure described above is re-iterated in many other roadmaps, but it is appropriate at this stage to show how another team went about it.

A good example of a recent technology specific roadmap is one in nanomaterials, which has now been published, having been on the Internet in draft form for a year. The 132 page report, resulting from workshops, was produced by around 100 people over 3 days; with introductions to the process, drawing up goals, and establishing the barriers, being completed on the first day, with a lunch time start. The health, safety, and environmental issues raised in this roadmap are discussed in more detail later in this book.

The goals were summarized as:

- Identify and enable early commercialisation opportunities *(catalysis, coatings, electronic and optical displays, medical diagnostics)*
- Achieve predictability and control of key building block properties *(chemical composition, size, shape, morphology, "surface chemistry")*
- Achieve predictability of life-time of nanomaterials under operating conditions
- Develop nanostructured materials that replace organic polymers in photonic devices
- Develop nanomaterials that increase energy storage in portable batteries by three times.

The general barriers were also recorded:

- Insufficient understanding to enable prediction of needed

properties, and how to achieve them
- Inadequate characterisation capabilities
- Insufficient knowledge to synthesise complex heterogeneous structures
- Achieving directed self assembly of building blocks and higher assemblies.

The whole of the second day focused on the R&D needs, leading to a research strategy. There is a great deal of detail in the draft report but the priority research items for nanomaterials were identified as:

- Develop capability to determine applications enabling properties *(modelling, synthesis, characterisation and functional testing)*
- Develop capability to predict and control enabling properties *(modelling, synthesis and characterisation)*
- Expand the type and number of organic and inorganic nanomaterial building blocks to enable new applications
- Develop and incorporate self assembly capability at the interface of building blocks
- Develop nanomaterial building blocks that enable self repair of coating structures at the micron and millimetre level.

In view of the strong focus on commercialisation of nanomaterials, the priority areas for potential exploitation were highlighted as:

- Catalysis *(broad range, early opportunity)*
- Separations *(sorbents and membranes)*
- Coatings *(early opportunity)*
- High performance materials *(strong, light weight, thermally and electrically conducting)*
- Energy conversion and storage
- Pharmaceutical and medical materials
- Sensors *(chemical, environmental, bio)*

- Optical and electronic displays *(early opportunity)*.

The following half-day was spent discussing the recommendations and the next steps for the roadmap. After exposure to other parties through the web, the full report was finally issued after a year, in December 2003, and is a very comprehensive 93 page report.

The procedure used was as previously described:

Where are we now?
Where should we be?
What is stopping us getting there?
What is needed to overcome the barriers?

TECHNOLOGY ROADMAPPING PROCEDURE

As stated earlier, all technology roadmaps follow a similar procedure. Where they differ is in the number of people involved and the time taken to produce them. The topic being considered can, of course, influence both those variables.

A procedure that has been found to work well is described below.

'Roadmapping Made Easy' Procedure

There are few establishments that have not gone through cost cutting, downsizing and re-engineering in order to remain competitive. As a result, they are much more sensitive to how they spend their time and money, and it has made them realise that they need better strategies either to remain in business or stay ahead of their competition. Most realise that they need technology roadmapping.

However, constraints on people's time and the cost of having large groups of experts tied up for several days on a technology roadmapping exercise, although important to the establishment's future, is not always seen as the most efficient way of achieving objectives.

As a result, the following procedure for technology roadmapping has proven to be a less time consuming, comprehensive way of establishing a technology roadmap in any field, with around 50 roadmaps having been completed for the EU's SMART FP6 Programme, some for the UK's Knowledge Transfer Networks, and the South African Government. The process takes only one day of a group of people's time, and further input, as with most roadmaps, is sought through the Internet or trade journals.

As with all roadmaps, they are working documents which are reviewed and added to as situations change. In some industries annual updates are necessary.

Participants

As described in Figure 2.1, technology roadmaps tend to fall into three groups

- Industry sector
- Technology specific
- Product

The type of roadmap has an influence on the number of people involved in the roadmapping session, but it must remain a manageable group. About 30 to 40 people can be easily managed at any one time. From experience, 25 is a good working number, but useful "starter" roadmaps can be produced by fewer than 10 participants. Sometimes smaller groups are more productive if the participants are selected for their knowledge and expertise.

The participants need to be those closely involved in the subject under consideration, and preferably from all aspects of the topic. For example, a technology roadmap should not just have participants from the Research and Development Department; it should include marketing personnel and some involvement from manufacturing, and possible supply chain people. "Buy-in" is crucial, so it is important not to miss out any key people that could diminish the exercise afterwards with any adverse criticism. It is also essential that the CEO is on board with the event; not necessarily attend-

30

ing, but being kept informed, feeling part of it, and appreciating its importance.

Methodology

The meeting should begin with each participant giving a brief description of who they are and what they do. This is followed with the facilitator going through the reasons for producing a technology roadmap and a summary of the process.

The methodology, which is colour coded, is the same as was shown in Figure 2.1. However, Figure 2.3, indicates that the process is simply a variant of a SWOT analysis. The Strengths and Weaknesses are identified in the first step – **Where are we now?** and the Opportunities are highlighted in the section on **Where do we want to be?** The Threats come from the stage asking **What is stopping us getting there?** Finally, the actions arising emanate from the last question.

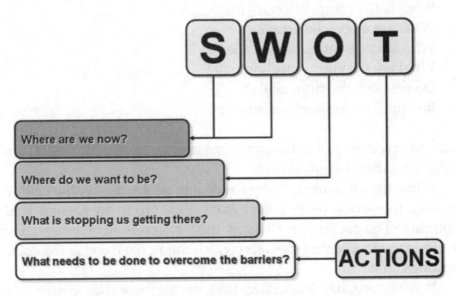

Figure 2.3: SWOT type analysis

Where are we now?

With all the benchmarking exercises that have been carried out over the last few years, it would be surprising if the audience of experts in the specific area under consideration were not well aware of their current status. However, all aspects of the current position need to be understood by all participants. It is helpful if one or more of the experts present gives a talk on the "state of the art", but if not, the facilitator should be able to draw out the main points, having carried out a survey of what has been published already in the specific area under consideration.

This is followed by splitting the team into small groups. For example, if there are 24 participants then 4 groups of 6 would be ideal. Each group is asked to come up with their thoughts as to where the subject under consideration is at this time.

Typical questions might be:

- Who are our present customers?
- What are the current trends?
- What are the main drivers?
- What is the competition up to?
- What are our niche areas?
- Who are present leaders in the field?
- What are the gaps in technology?
- Do we have the right skills?
- Is capital investment sufficient?

Each group records their thoughts on large hexagonal "Post-its", and in this case they are green ones.

When the ideas of each group seem to be drying up, the facilitator asks the scribe (note taker) from each group to present their thoughts. The facilitator clusters the hexagons in a honeycomb fashion around a central hexagon which might have one of the above headings on it.

It is particularly important that the scribe writes clearly and summarises each input in an understandable way, with only one

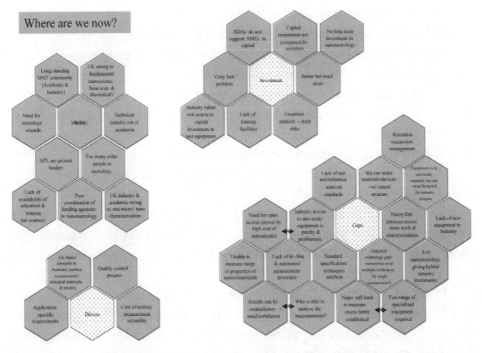

Figure 2.4: Use of hexagons to cluster ideas

thought on each hexagon.

Of course, if there are several groups there will be some repetition and there is no need to add those to the chart that the facilitator is producing. At this stage then, the wall should include a large number of grouped hexagons as illustrated in Figure 2.4.

This method of clustering ideas is just one method commonly used in brainstorming exercises.

Where do we want to be?

For this stage of the roadmapping procedure, it is important to gather the vision and aspirations of the team, and again this is carried out with the same hexagon brainstorming procedure, but this time with pink hexagons.

The sorts of questions that need answering are:

- What is our vision for the future?
- What should we be doing to maximise benefits?
- Are we doing something now that we should put more effort into?
- Are we doing something currently that we should drop?
- What technologies are going to make a real impact on our activities?
- What new areas should we be working in?
- Are there opportunities for creating spin-out companies?

This is an important stage and the facilitator will be able to judge when to draw the session to a close. One thing that is certain is that there will be a lot of discussion when each group presents its hexagons.

Having agreed the thoughts from the whole team, it is necessary to add priorities to them, and to do this each of the small groups are given a limited number of adhesive dots to stick on the hexagons that they feel are most important. This sets the priorities for this section of the roadmap.

What is stopping us getting there?

The procedure is the same for this stage except it might be wise to move participants around to form different groups. It tends to refresh the groups and aid networking opportunities.

This part is all about looking at the barriers that are likely to prevent the group reaching their goals. Anything that is likely to inhibit them should be extracted. Again it is helpful to have 'prompts' such as:

- What are the gaps in our technology?
- Do we have the skilled people we need?
- Is funding likely to be adequate?
- Do we have the necessary infrastructure?

All thoughts are, as before, gathered on hexagons - this time they are

What needs to be done to overcome the barriers?

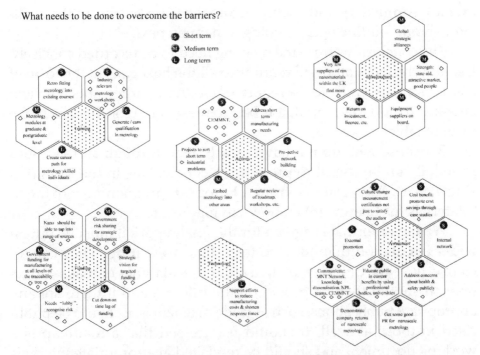

Figure 2.5: Clusters of main issues with time scales

yellow ones. Again the priority issues are marked by each group, using "sticky" dots for the more important points on the hexagons. In this way it is possible to gain a consensus of views.

What needs to be done to overcome the barriers?

The same procedure is adopted but this time the hexagons are blue! Consideration needs to be given to both technical and non-technical solutions to overcoming the barriers. For this section, the timescales are particularly important.

It is helpful to ask the participants to place stickers on the hexagons to indicate which are short, medium or long-term issues. As a result the final hexagons might appear as exemplified in Figure 2.5.

From experience, most participants find the roadmapping

exercise stimulating and useful. Before the team breaks up the facilitator should outline what is going to happen next.

The conclusions from the meeting need to be recorded concisely. Usually, the facilitator will reproduce all the hexagons in the form of charts as an appendix to the report, but for non-participants who will be asked to add their input, it is best to present the conclusions in the form of tables.

For those who do not have time to read through all the issues raised, it can be useful to present the conclusions in the form of a single chart. A typical one from a European programme looking at 'Materials for Energy' (5) is shown in Figure 2.6.

Whatever format is agreed for the final report, it must be put on wider circulation than just the team that drew it up. They can, of course, have the first view of it, in order to add things or make corrections. It should then be posted on the Internet and if there are any appropriate publications, such as trade magazines, it should be publicised in those as well. It should be stressed that a roadmap is a working document and should be re-visited at appropriate intervals and updated to retain its usefulness.

Experience shows that data collected from even relatively small samples of experts is very representative of the current state of the technology and with provisions can used on a national or wider scale. However, as already stated, this method only provides a timely snapshot. It is valuable to retain the group of experts who provide the initial roadmapping data to form a permanent focus group to monitor progress and provide updates when necessary. This was done with a number of groups in the UK in 2005 as part of the strategy of the MNT Network programme.

METHODOLOGY USE FOR INTERNATIONAL ROADMAPPING

Collecting material for the international roadmaps referred to in Chapter 1 requires a different technique to that described above. For

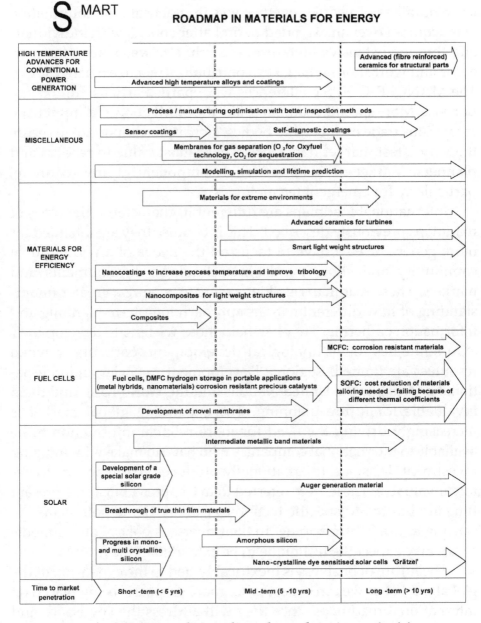

Figure 2.6: Typical time-line chart showing priorities

example, the production of MANCEF Roadmaps necessitated input from over 300 contributors from different countries so bringing such large numbers of people together was impractical. The information was acquired over an extended period after contact with individuals and through extensive literature research. Use was made of conferences and workshops where key contributors met to exchange ideas. The MANCEF–COMS conferences were particularly useful for that purpose. More specific roadmaps, like the SEMI one, used input from the various trade membership bodies. Here it was important to secure the very latest market data since it is of most value to readers and planners. Market trends are a vital component of any roadmap, particularly for emergent technologies.

International roadmaps are different in character to the types of roadmaps previously described. This is because they are intended for more general use so have to focus on the needs of a wider global community and show trends in technology developments and markets. These roadmaps enable readers to acquire a greater understanding of how different nations approach long-term planning and information gathering. They can help those wishing to develop their own strategies for technological development, particularly when resources are limited. Regional Development Agencies and international bodies like the United Nations and the World Bank find them invaluable for future planning. The expanding global market is increasingly driving the need for more reliable information to be available to international companies who have to make wide-ranging investment decisions. Internationally produced roadmaps are therefore invaluable. These were referred to in Chapter 1 but at the present time are limited to specific technology areas. Some politicians are starting to use 'roadmapping' in their overseas policy commitments so we may expect the technique to be extended in the future.

The future of business is inextricably tied to the expansion of the global market so we can expect to see more emphasis being placed on international roadmaps since they will address the key issues and challenges facing the world community. The recent problems with the US and European banking systems and their dramatic affect on the world's financial markets have highlighted the weaknesses in the operation of the global system. Perhaps the use of a roadmapping process for international finance might have identified the underlying problems early enough to have avoided the path that led to the problems. Such problems will always exist when governments, leading bankers and financiers work independently in a free market with minimal regulation. The lack of shared knowledge and foresight means planning is replaced by speculation and immediate responses to the eccentricity of the stock markets with the inevitable disastrous consequences.

The methodology used for non-technology roadmaps may need to be changed but basically the principles are the same. The financial world has an excellent communications and computer network which is basic to its operation. Many decades of market data therefore exists on which to build a knowledge base. Roadmapping the future of financial markets will be more difficult than technology markets but there is a synergy between them, related to the need to find ways of creating wealth through economic development. It can be expected in the wake of the current crisis with its global consequences that more attention will be given to the value of strategic planning which is core to roadmapping.

REFERENCES

1   http://en.wikipedia.org/wiki/Delphi.
2   Smith, A, *Mapping out the Future for the Road* Ahead, Materials World, 2003, Vol. 11, No. 10, 2003.
3   *Technology Roadmap for Materials of Construction, Operation and Maintenance in the Chemical Process Industry.*
    http://www.chemicalvision2020.org/pdfs/matconst.pdf
4   *Chemical Industry R&D Roadmap in Nanomaterials by Design*
    http://www.chemicalvision2020.org/pdfs/nano_roadmap.pdf
5   European SMART Consortium, *Materials powering Europe*, March 2007
    http://www.smart-ssa.net/datapool/page/9/Proceedings_Energy.pdf

CHAPTER 3

ROADMAPS IN MATERIALS AND CHEMICAL PROCESSES

CONTENTS

BACKGROUND

There are a large number of roadmaps freely available which relate to materials and the chemicals sector. Many governments have identified materials as one of the 'pillars' in their strategic thinking, so there is a wide variety of technology roadmaps covering the many aspects materials will have on our future lives.

Several of the roadmaps are quite general; others cover specific industry sectors, while there are a large number that focus on different issues relating to materials and chemicals. Those summarised in this chapter are arranged by their date of publication.

ROADMAPS

Technology Roadmap for Computational Fluid Dynamics

The Chemical Industry in the US prepared a vision of how it would meet the increasing competitive challenges through to 2020. This was entitled *Technology Vision 2020: The US Chemical Industry* (1), and as a result further roadmaps were instigated to go into more detail for key areas. One of these was created in January 1999, for Computational Fluid Dynamics (2) with the main aim of de-bottlenecking in chemical plants. Under consideration were fluid flow situations which comprise liquids, gases, solids or a combination of these phases. These can be reactive; turbulent or laminar; steady or unsteady; Newtonian or non-Newtonian, and the applications in chemical processing are: mixers and chemical reactors; packed beds; crystallizing / dissolving equipment; pneumatic conveyors and classifiers; flows in pipes; sprays; and biological systems.

Alternative Media, Conditions and Raw Materials Workshop

The Green Chemistry Institute in the US used the Vision 2020 model to hold a workshop to look at sustainable development in the Chemical Industry. A report in the same format as the other Vision 2020 roadmaps was made public in July 1999 (3), and tabulated the R&D needs under the headings:

- Alternative cleaning and dissolution methods
- Alternative reaction media in chemical synthesis
- Alternative material modification / pollutant sequestration
- R&D needs to overcome key barriers – electro-technology and alternative conditions
- Research needs:
  - Polymer modelling
  - Improved / benign polymer processing / synthesis
  - Alternative reaction media polymerisation
  - Alternative raw materials / new science.

Technology Roadmap for Computational Chemistry
In September 1999, the US Chemical Industry produced a technology roadmap for Computational Chemistry (4) to promote:

- Shortened product and process development cycles
- Optimisation of existing processes, to improve energy efficiency and minimise waste
- Efficient design of new products and processes
- Improvement of health, safety, and environment aspects.

Applications of importance were seen as: New Bioprocesses; Catalyst Design; Improved Reaction Mechanisms; Product Development (polymers, pharmaceuticals); Efficient Process Design; Materials and Polymer Design; Polymer Processing; Environmental Modelling and Remediation.

Vision 2020 – 2000 Separations Roadmap
In 2000, the Centre for Waste Reduction Technologies of AIChE (the American Institute of Chemical Engineers) produced a roadmap on Separations (5) which is an update of a 1998 exercise. It examines seven separation technologies (adsorption, crystallisation, distillation, extraction, membranes, separative reactors, and ion exchange). In addition, two cross-cutting areas, bio-separations and dilute

solutions, are examined. For a number of these areas new materials are a feature of the high priority research needs.

Technology Roadmap for Coatings on Glass

Sandia National Laboratories reported (6) on a meeting held in January 2000, which engaged a group of experts active in glass coatings. The workshop had break-out sessions covering:

- Flat glass
- Container glass
- Coatings on glass fibre
- Speciality coatings on glass.

Key needs that span the industry, that were identified include:

- Data bases of information concerning film properties (optical, mechanical, electrical, etc.) and deposition chemistries
- A pilot-scale facility for developing new coating processes
- Computational methods for rapid screening of potential coating materials
- Rapid prototyping methods for evaluating coating processes
- Fundamental data concerning deposition processes
- Improved understanding of surfaces and interfaces
- Low-cost deposition methods
- Sophisticated sensors and process control.

Petroleum – Industry of the Future

In February 2000, a draft Technology Roadmap for the Petroleum Industry was published and has formed the basis for the industry leaders' roadmap entitled *Petroleum – Industry of the Future* (7).

The high priority research needs for this very large industry sector are:

- Energy and process efficiency
- Environmental performance
- Materials and inspection technology
- Distribution system and retail delivery services
- New separation technologies for refining.

For the later the key goal is to use membranes which are expected to be 20% more energy efficient than distillation.

Technology Roadmap for Canadian Metalcasting

Industry Canada has sponsored a number of roadmaps in fields that are regarded as strategic to the future of Canada. This technology roadmap was produced in August 2000 (8), and a major conclusion was that virtually any Canadian metal caster could potentially attain world class status and successfully compete in both the domestic and export marketplace. There is emphasis on finding high-value areas in which to work, and also on improving the Canadian infrastructure to aid progress. Environmental issues were also going to be addressed.

Technology Roadmap for Materials

In August 2000, this roadmap was published as another part of the US Chemical Industry Vision 2020 programme (9). The focus is on the following areas:

- New materials
  - Explore new concepts in catalysis for polymers
  - Study of polymer-structure property relationships
  - Colloid / interfacial science
  - Continued development of composite technology for non-military applications
  - Continued development of new materials
- Materials characterisation
  - R&D tools
  - Real-time measurements

47

- Materials modelling and prediction
  - Methods development
  - Theory
- Additives
  - Prediction / modelling
  - Interfacial methods / fundamentals applied to additives
  - Nanoparticles
- Disassembly, recovery and recycle
  - Collection of raw materials
  - Deriving pure monomers and intermediates from polymers
  - Chemistry of mixed polymer streams and polymer modification
  - High yield separation processes.

As with other roadmaps based on the Vision 2020 format, there is considerable detail in the text of the report.

Technology Roadmap for Advanced Ceramics
The Advanced Ceramics Technology Roadmap (10) was developed for the US Advanced Ceramic Association in December 2000, and sets out the research, development and demonstrations needed for improving advanced structural ceramics.

The ambitions are that by 2020, advanced ceramics will be the cost effective, preferred materials in demanding applications of industry, such as power generation, aerospace, transport, military, and consumer products. Design methods, property testing standards, and property databases should be available so a team (including a designer, supplier, and end-user) can select a ceramic that will meet the application requirements, and provide superior benefits compared to alternate materials (such as metals, polymers). Ceramics will be able to be fabricated into complex and large shapes with minimum development time and minimum defects. Non-destructive techniques will be able to detect small critical defects and bolster production efficiencies, and end-users will have experience and confidence in using ceramics.

New Biocatalysts – Essential Tools for a Sustainable 21st Century Chemical Industry

The New Biocatalysts strategic plan was published in 2000 (11), to help expand their use in a wider variety of chemical processes. At the time examples of such processes were production of high-fructose corn syrup, aspartame, semi-synthetic penicillins, and some cancer drugs. The goals of the group of experts were:

- Develop biocatalysts which are better, faster, and cheaper than current chemical catalysts
- Develop a tool-box of biocatalysts to cover a broad range of reactions
- Increase temperature stability, activity, and solvent compatibility
- Develop molecular modelling to provide rapid design of new enzymes
- Create better tools for new biocatalyst development
- Educate the public about the social benefits of using biocatalysts.

Roadmap for New Processes Chemistry

In July 2001, New Process Chemistry was the subject of another roadmap in the US Chemical Industry Vision 2020 series (12). To stimulate interest in new processes, the report highlights the example of Ibuprofen. A new process was developed that had only three catalytic steps and 80% atom utilisation, replacing the old six-step process that gave 40% atom utilisation. The new route also provided around 30% energy savings, and there was virtually no waste. The report details the R&D priorities under the following headings:

- Novel feedstocks
- Reaction media
- Process conditions and equipment
- Cross-cutting R&D.

The results are presented diagrammatically, and as with other Vision 2020 roadmaps, the priorities are listed as top, high, and medium.

49

Technology Roadmap for Combinatorial Methods

In September 2001, another roadmap was published, in the US Chemical Industry's Vision 2020 series on combinatorial methods (abbreviated to 'combi' in the report) as an enabling tool to accelerate the discovery process (13). Combinatorial chemistry had played an increasingly important role in the screening and discovery of new drugs. It was seen that it had the potential to revolutionize the design process for new chemicals, materials, and catalysts. The driver was that combinatorial methodologies could shorten the discovery phase of research and development from 2 to 3 years to 3 to 6 months. The vision for 2020 was:

- The cost of combi must be reduced
- Combi should be used to explore complex systems
- High throughput experiments should be possible throughout an organization, with understanding of output
- Combi should be explored for process-based applications
- Students should be educated in combinatorial techniques
- All groups (industry, academia, and government) should be engaged in combi efforts
- Combi should be web-enabled
- Combi should be coupled with molecular modelling
- Materials supply should be seamlessly integrated with end-user needs
- Part of materials funding should be extended to combi
- Faster scale-up must be achieved
- Combi should have the capability to solve pilot-plant / scale-up issues
- There must be completely new thinking about how discovery is carried out
- The number of products that need to be screened to get to market should be quantified
- Computers should be loaded with algorithms, models, data, etc., and used routinely for screening / predictions.

Roadmap for Reaction Engineering

The Centre for Waste Reduction Technologies of AIChE (the American Institute of Chemical Engineers) produced a second roadmap in 2001 on Reaction Engineering (14).

The priority research needs are summarized below:

- Basic Chemicals: Develop more efficient methods to build process models, obtain and predict physical, chemical, and transport property data and to verify model results.
- Speciality Chemicals: Develop models to predict product properties a priori, to facilitate reactor / process selection and design, and to increase reaction selectivity.
- Pharmaceuticals: Develop better experimental screening techniques to reduce development time and costs.
- Polymers: Link process conditions to product; develop better fluid dynamics models that account for interaction effects of large complex molecules; and create monitors that can track polymerisation progress on line.
- Reactor System Design and Scale-up: Establish better procedures for characterising the operation of laboratory, pilot and plant reactors. Develop more efficient methods to obtain physical, chemical, and transport property data for input into and verification of models.
- Chemical Mechanisms: Develop micro-kinetic experimental capabilities; methods to integrate solvent effects into reaction models; tools to couple process chemistry and modelling; and methods to determine macroscopic properties and kinetic behaviour from molecular structures.
- Catalysis: Develop better in situ characterization and sensing tools; system integration techniques to optimise catalyst and reactor operations simultaneously.
- Novel Reactors: Research areas include intensified reactors; rapid heating and cooling techniques; structured contacting; external field-assisted and photochemical reactions; and reactors for extreme conditions. Enabling technologies

51

include new materials development, systems integration, micro-scale properties and phenomena determination, multistage design capabilities, and self-assembling reactor development.

Roadmap for Alumina Technology

This roadmap, published in 2001, was compiled by the US Department of Energy and the Australian Department of Industry, Science and Resources (15). It is a more generic roadmap and includes aspects of roadmaps carried out by the industry in inert anodes, advanced smelting technology, use of aluminium in automotive markets, handling and treatment of bauxite residue, use of advanced ceramics to improve production and processing; all of which are referenced in the bibliography of their report.

The highest priorities are set out diagrammatically, and identified as near, mid, and long term under key headings:

- Bayer process chemistry and alternatives
- Resource utilisation
- Energy efficiency
- Process and knowledge management
- Residue treatment and re-use
- Safety / human exposure.

Technology Roadmap (Powder Metallurgy and Particulate Materials) and PM² Industry Vision

The PM² industry fabricates products using several different technologies, including pressing and sintering, injection moulding, hot isostatic pressing, and forging. The vision, in their roadmap (16), is to become the preferred source of net-shaped metal-based systems to bring high-value components to a diverse customer base. The strategy has three main thrusts:

- Enhanced material properties and performance
- Improved manufacturing and processing

- Enabling technologies and infrastructure.

To achieve the vision, a broad range of research is required and is presented under six themes:

- Increased material options
- Shift to flexible, agile manufacturing
- Expand design and processing capabilities
- Improve supply chain efficiencies
- Focus on emerging product needs
- Cultivate critical industry resources.

The roadmap is particularly well set out, and each R&D priority is accompanied by a brief description, the impact it could have on goals, key technical elements, and an implementation diagram showing the involvement of PM^2, Government, and potential partners.

Technology Roadmap for the Glass Industry
In 1997 the Glass Industry in the US held a workshop to plan out a technology roadmap for their sector. One result from the workshop was that in 1998 the Glass Manufacturing Industry Council (GMIC) was established under the auspices of the American Ceramic Society. After a number of updates to the outcomes from the initial workshop, the roadmap was published in April 2002 (17), and examines the potential research and development needs for the subsequent twenty years.
Four elements define the central strategy:

- Production Efficiency – undertake R&D that will enable the industry become more efficient, productive, and competitive
- Energy Efficiency - identify and adopt technologies to make substantial improvements
- Environmental Performance - achieve cleaner operations with lower environmental control costs and increase glass recycling.

- Innovative Uses – develop new applications for glass that provide increased profitability.

The roadmap reports specific targets for these issues, with the intention of ensuring that the industry will survive and prosper in the intensely competitive and challenging global marketplace. Specific technology challenges are identified, and under 'Innovative Uses', communications and electronics, structural uses, novel uses, surfaces and coatings, and advanced processing and control are listed.

Technology Roadmap for Immobilisation in Catalysis

Substantive manufacturing was the main driver for a roadmap on Immobilisation in Catalysis, which was carried out in July 2003 by the BHR Group in the UK (18), with a focus on enabling catalysts and reagents to be recovered and re-used while facilitating their separation from the product. Immobilised catalysts can be used in a variety of reactor configurations at high catalyst concentrations and hence high volumetric productivities, which leads to lower costs. Integration of measurement and modelling techniques was the main feature underpinning the vision for the future.

Roadmap for Process Equipment Materials Technology

Another roadmap spawned from the US Chemical Industry Vision 2020 exercise addressed the need for chemical plants to last longer under the severe conditions many of them were working under. The roadmap was first issued in December 1998, but was updated in October 2003 (19).

In many ways this is a model roadmap, listing performance targets, technology challenges, and separating the priority R&D items into near term (0-3 years), mid term (3-10 years) and long term (> 10 years). The research priorities are categorized under the following headings:

- Knowledge management
- Prediction of materials degradation

- Condition assessment, and the effects of design, fabrication and maintenance of asset integrity
- New materials for challenging process conditions.

Many of the priority R&D topics identified cut across several technical areas, and are addressed by a number of "grand challenges", which are large, integrated, multi-partner, multi-disciplinary R&D activities that incorporate more than one R&D element, but attempt to achieve a single broad goal.

Technology Roadmap for Steel Industry
The Steel Industry in North America produced a Technology Roadmap in 2001 (20), and in October 2003, in accordance with all good roadmaps, was updated to reflect progress and changing market situations (21). It still represents a sub-set of the original roadmap and focuses on barriers and pathways for yield improvements. The key opportunities for yield improvements are outlined under the following headings:

Modelling, Measurement, and Control
- Robust, low-cost sensors to measure key ironmaking and steelmaking parameters (chemistry, temperature, etc.)
- Real-time off-gas analysis methods and chemistry adjustment methods
- Detection systems to detect and classify inclusions
- Process control practices that reduce shape defects
- Improved control of heat treatment processes for precise control of properties
- Advanced combustion control systems for furnaces.

Operating Techniques and Practices
- Optimisation of energy use
- Techniques to minimise or eliminate scaling
- Technology to eliminate casting or oscillation marks
- Improved furnace heat transfer.

Process Equipment
- Longer-lasting refractories that do not interact with steel or slag.
- Other materials and technologies that reduce maintenance requirements
- Technologies that allow higher rolling speeds and faster processing in other processes
- Higher productivity RHF operations

Fuels, Feedstocks, and Recycling
- Improved understanding of coal injection to the blast furnace
- Economical processes for recycling ironmaking and steel-making by-products
- Recycling spent pickle liquor to produce a higher value by-product.

Material Properties and Manufacturing Technologies
- Improved microstructure control
- Reliable property data for advanced steels.

Technology Roadmap for Low Energy Polymer Processing
In December 2003, Faraday Plastics Partnership provided a roadmap to set about the wastage in polymer processing. An update was carried out in June 2005, but with the demise of the Faraday Partnerships it was never published. The 2003 roadmap was available through their web site but cannot now be accessed. However, it was a very successful roadmap, in that within six months of its completion it successfully gained European funding to tackle the problems.

The original roadmap contained the following priority conclusions:

- It is necessary to understand the true energy balance for extrusion, injection moulding, and other polymer processing techniques
- Fewer processing steps are needed

- Save energy by being successful first time – avoid reprocessing
- Have effective thermal insulation
- Use the right screw for a particular job
- Use 'intelligent' additives
- Reduce the amount of polymer where practicable.

Technology Roadmap for Rubber

Under the auspices of the UK's Institute of Materials, Minerals and Mining, a roadmap was produced in 2003 to maximise the success of the UK rubber industry sector (22). Trends at the time were recognised as lighter weight products for transport applications, one-piece tyre and wheel developments, insurance companies driving the trend to safer tyres (faster stop, improved road holding, 'intelligent' tyres), and landfill not being seen as an option for used tyres. Improved noise dampening products in cars and trains was seen as a development area for non-tyre applications, along with increasing activity through nanotechnology developments for barrier properties, and improved additives.

It was observed that a Foresight Vehicle Roadmap that was being prepared should be closely linked to the Rubber Roadmap since the former had little coverage on rubber materials.

Chemical Industry R&D Roadmap for Nanomaterials by Design

A further roadmap, on Nanomaterials by Design, was produced by the US Chemical Industry Vision 2020 Technology Partnership in December 2003 (23). This is one of the best produced roadmaps, involving a large number of people and being set out in an easily readable form. 'Nanomaterials by Design' refers to creating structures with nanoscale features that provide unique functionality and utility for target applications. The following items summarise the priority research requirements:

Fundamental understanding and synthesis:
- Understanding of nanoscale structure-property-processing relationships

- Experimentally validated models and theories of nanoscale physics and chemistry
- New paradigms for creating nanoscale building blocks
- Design strategies for controlled assembly – nanocomposites, spatially resolved nanostructures
- High throughput screening methods to determine structure-property relationships
- Performance evaluation at the laboratory scale
- Compendium of methods to synthesise and assemble nanomaterials

Manufacturing and processing:
- Unit operations and robust scale-up and scale-down methods
- Manufacturing techniques for hierarchical assembly
- Dispersion and surface modification processes that retain functionality
- Process monitoring and controls for consistency

Characterisation tools:
- Real-time characterisation methods and tools
- Infrastructure for tool development and use

Modelling and simulation:
- Fundamental models to accurately predict nanostructure formation
- Bridging models between scales – from atoms to self assembly to devices
- Infrastructure to support model advancement

Environment, safety and health:
- Assessment of human health and environmental impact hazards
- Determination of exposure potentials for nano-sized materials

- Handling guidelines for operations involving nanomaterials

Standards and informatics:
- Standard procedures for nanomaterial synthesis
- Reference materials for property measurement
- Standard methods for physical and chemical property evaluation
- Computational standards to improve information processing and transfer
- Standards for material evaluation in application
- Standardised internationally recognised nomenclature
- Infrastructure to foster standardisation

Knowledge and technology transfer:
- Technology transfer policies to foster commercialisation
- Infrastructure to encourage knowledge sharing

Education and training:
- Educated and trained workforce
- Greater public and industry awareness

In the report these priorities are given a timeframe along with a rough estimate of the relative costs of each priority.

Technology Roadmap for Advanced Ceramics
The Powdermatrix Faraday Partnership in the UK produced a series of four roadmaps in 2004, designed to ensure a healthy future for specific areas of interest. For Advanced Ceramics (24), the sector comprises two main categories of materials: structural ceramics and functional ceramics. The roadmap confirmed the industry demand to grow businesses through diversification and improved manufacturing. Recommended actions to grow the market were:

- Co-ordinate efforts for better consistency and quality of

products and processes to improve manufacturing processes
- Stimulate development of innovative manufacturing processes, focusing on smaller product runs, reducing processing steps and shortening product development cycles
- Develop materials in key areas of growth, such as nano-structured ceramics, fuel cells, biomaterials, membranes and catalysis.
- Analyse and disseminate information on emerging key markets and opportunities.

Technology Roadmap for Hardmetals

Also in 2004, Powdermatrix issued a roadmap on Hardmetals (25), which was influenced by two product areas that were of interest to the UK market: wear parts and cutting tools. Key technologies expected to impact on the future competitiveness of the industry were:

- Alternative non-toxic binders
- Coated hardmetal powders
- Alternative powder production methods
- Products arising from nanopowders
- Surface engineered hardmetals
- Surface engineered products competitive with monolithic hardmetals
- Novel reclamation and recycling processes
- In-line non-destructive testing
- Metal injection moulding process development
- Innovative energy efficient manufacturing processes.

Technology Roadmap for Magnetics Sector

The Powdermatrix roadmap for the UK's Magnetics Sector was also published in 2004 (26), and only deals with bulk magnetic materials and their applications, not thin films and the potential for spintronics. It was recommended that the UK Government should provide a strategic commitment to the following key technologies:

- Improved efficiency in aerospace and land based power generation
- Develop new soft metal composite processing technology for more efficient motors
- Develop a capability to recycle commercial magnets for magnetic materials of high intrinsic value.

Technology Roadmap for Powder Metal Sector
A further Powdermatrix roadmap on Powder Metals (PM) was released in 2004 (27) and identified three sectors of importance to UK industry: high production volume, PM structural parts, and gas turbine components manufactured from powder feedstocks. For PM structural parts, the key actions were:

- Identification of opportunities for high margin, niche products
- Developments aimed at moving the powder metal business into new products, such as
  - High performance structural parts (e.g. enhanced fatigue performance)
  - Cost effective routes to complex parts (e.g. 3-D geometries)
  - Light alloy PM products, titanium and aluminium based
  - New soft magnetic PM products.

Roadmap for Green Chemical Technology
The Crystal Faraday Partnership (now part of the Chemistry Innovation Knowledge Transfer Network in the UK) produced a Green Chemical Technology Roadmap in 2004 for the UK Chemical Industry (28). OECD defines green chemistry as *"the design, manufacture and use of environmentally benign chemical products and processes that prevent pollution, produce less hazardous waste and reduce environmental*

and human health risks". The areas of green chemistry identified as being able to change the sustainability of the Chemical Industry were:

- Green product design – minimising environmental impact
- Feedstocks – substituting renewable for non-renewable
- Novel reaction
- Novel catalysis
- Solvents
- Process improvement
- Separation technology
- Enabling technologies.

These technology areas would be critical in reducing: product toxicity; environmental impact of a product; raw materials; use of non-renewable resources; waste and emissions; energy used in manufacture; risk and hazard; and life-cycle costs of a chemical plant.

A Technology Roadmap for Colloid and Interface Science in the UK
Also in 2004, the Impact Faraday Partnership, which is also now part of the UK's Chemistry Innovation Knowledge Transfer Network, produced a roadmap for Colloid and Interface Science (29). The dominant research themes in this comprehensive report were:

- Prediction modelling
- Controlled colloid architecture
- Controlled and triggered release
- Measurement
- Biological systems.

Detail within these themes opened up opportunities to link to other parts of the UK Chemical Industry.

A Roadmap for High Throughput Technologies
The Insight Faraday Partnership is also now part of the UK's Chemistry

Innovation Knowledge Transfer Network, and it too produced a roadmap in 2004. It is entitled 'A Roadmap for High Throughput Technologies' but does not appear to be still available via the web, however enquiries should be sent through the KTN web site 'contacts' section (30). High Throughput Technology (HTT) can deliver:

- Faster discovery and optimisation of new compounds and materials with specific properties and effects
- Thorough investigation of parameters relating to new processes
- New science which would be difficult to achieve with conventional equipment and processes.

The roadmap considers the impact of HTT on industrial sectors, and the requirements for new or improved HTT capabilities are tabled for the following areas: synthesis, catalysis, bioassay, formulation, analysis, materials, and process engineering.

Technology Roadmap for Nanocomposites
This roadmap is no longer available on the web since the UK's Faraday Plastics Partnership no longer exists. Carried out in 2005, the Nanocomposites Technology Roadmap drew together a number of experts in the field, and the general conclusions were that the UK needed a boost in this sector because there was a lack of awareness of the benefits of nanocomposite materials, which was not helped by the general slump in the polymer industry.

It was recommended that a generic research programme should be set up to address relevant issues such as: processing, modelling, health and safety, applications development, materials development, characterisation, environmental profile and life cycle analysis, long term behaviour, development of standards, and design.

Roadmap Report in Thin Films and Coatings (EU Nanoroadmap Project)
In November 2005, a series of roadmaps, concerned with nanotech-

nology, was produced under the European Commission's Sixth Framework Programme for different aspects of materials, energy, and health and medical systems. For the materials sector four roadmaps were constructed, and were published as a single booklet. They are available through the web (31). All the roadmaps used the same format, where a Delphi questionnaire methodology was primarily employed to obtain the views of a number of experts.

For the Thin Films and Coatings Roadmap, a definition of thin films was given, followed by what the experts judged were the most important properties of thin films e.g. chemical, magnetic, optical, mechanical, and heat resistance. The types of films were based on polymers, metal oxide ceramics, metals, silicates, carbon, etc.

The pipeline for thin films and coatings was taken into account: production and application, post-treatment, patterning, and market application. Typical production processes are physical vapour deposition (PVD), chemical vapour deposition (CVD), or sol-gel, but other routes were considered.

The most relevant applications considered were:

- Thin film transistors
- Large area electronic devices
- Solar cells
- Planar waveguides
- Non-volatile memory
- Micro electro-mechanical systems
- Friction reducing surfaces
- Thermally insulated windows
- Self-cleaning surfaces.

As for the other roadmaps in this series, the experts' views of how the applications will develop over a ten year period are shown diagrammatically. For thin films and coatings the progress of developments is give as it is when the roadmap was drawn up, in five years time and after ten years. The later is reproduced below by way of example in Figure 3.1.

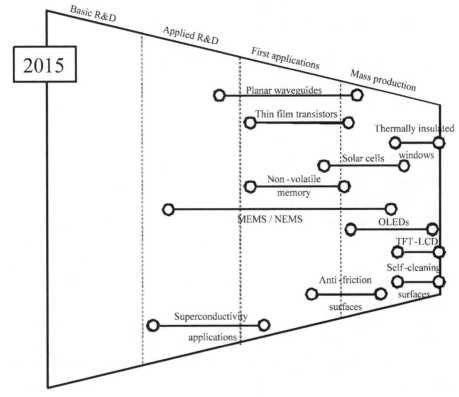

Figure 3.1

In addition the report examines the risk involved versus the expected growth in the next decade for each of the relevant applications, and they were also asked to comment on how good the EU was, relative to the rest of the world, in the thin films and coatings field. The main technical and other barriers are discussed, and final recommendations made. The following were highlighted:

- In non high-tech sectors (e.g. self-cleaning surfaces or thermal insulating applications) SMEs could play a stronger role
- Certain high potential applications that might soon be commercialised (self-cleaning coatings, new forms of solar

energy) also need more focused research

- The combination of transparency, possible through nanotechnology, with chemical, mechanical or thermal functionality, offers huge potential for exploitation
- EU has key strengths but as yet no ambitious research programmes
- In areas where large volumes, and where technologies have been demonstrated, R&D efforts should shift more towards scale-up facilities for production
- Fundamental research needed into understanding interactions at the molecular level
- Development of tools for both characterisation and production.

Roadmap Report in Nanoparticles / Nanocomposites (EU Nanoroadmap Project)

For the Nanoparticles /Nanocomposites Roadmap, it defines what is meant by nanoparticles since at that time a unique definition was not available. More recently, the British Standards Institute (BSi) has published a vocabulary for nanoparticles (32). The roadmap focuses on nanoparticles that are of most interest: metal oxide ceramics, metals, silicates, and non-oxide ceramics.

For each of these nanoparticle categories, the most exploitable properties were judged to be mechanical, chemical (reactivity), thermal, electrical, optical, magnetic, and specific surface area. The different steps in the nanoparticle pipeline are reviewed: production, functionalisation, integration into a nanocomposite material, and the particular application. For each step, detail is given on, for example, the host of different methods for production of nanoparticles, and for specific applications, they are listed under the following headings:

- Power / energy
- Healthcare / medical
- Engineering
- Consumer goods

- Environmental
- Electronics.

As with the Thin Films and Coatings Roadmap, an overview is given of the current applications, and the applications with timescales that are expected in five and ten years.

In the section on 'final conclusions and recommendations', the following comments are highlighted:

- Production yield of specific active sizes, and control of size distribution, would reduce waste and cost.
- On-line instrumentation would improve product consistency and performance
- Up-scaling of relevant processes is an issue that needs to enable Europe to bring nanoparticles to market
- Key capabilities that offer the most potential for improvement and resulting applications are fine control of nanoscale structure and functionalisation
- Increasing awareness of key players about opportunities offered by nanotechnology.

Roadmap Report in Nanoporous Materials (EU Nanoroadmap Project)

Using the same format, nanoporous materials are defined in this roadmap. They can be natural or synthetic, organic or inorganic, and hybrid materials. Bulk materials are carbon, silicon, silicates, polymers, metal oxides, organic / metals, organic / silicon, etc. Materials for membranes include zeolites or schwartzites. The most revolutionary properties of bulk nanoporous materials are increased surface area, absorbent, photonic structure / crystal, insulation, and light depending refractive index. For membranes the most interesting properties are increased surface area, absorbent, sieving, reduced weight, and photonic structure / crystal.

The pipeline for nanoporous materials was judged to be template preparation, material synthesis, functionalisation, and market applications. Some of the more important conclusions were:

- For large volume applications (catalysis and membranes), large industry involvement is essential because SMEs would not be able to take such long term investment
- Catalysis should be one of the main application-driven research topics
- Applications combining thermal insulation and structural properties of nanoporous materials should be targeted by high-tech SMEs
- The fields of instrumentation and equipment should also be of interest to SMEs
- A fundamental understanding of structure-property relationships is needed
- Priority should be given to research on environmentally friendly materials or hybrid materials.

Roadmap Report in Dendrimers (EU Nanoroadmap Project)
For this roadmap, a dendrimer is defined as a macromolecule, which is characterised by its highly branched 3D structure that provides a high degree of surface functionality and versatility. Its structure is always built around a multi-functional core molecule, with branches and end-groups.

- Exploitable properties of dendrimers are:
- Polyvalency – the outer shell can be multifunctional
- Defined architecture, size and shape control
- Mono-dispersibility – step-wise synthetic processes enable dendrimers with highly uniform sizes
- Loading capacity – can be used to carry and / or store a wide range of molecules
- Biocompatibility / low toxicity
- Transfection properties – transport genetic material into cell interiors.

Final conclusions and recommendations from the report were:

- Up-scaling of production is a key field of research for lowering costs
- Ability to rapidly produce new dendrimers templated to fit certain bio-molecules (to defend against pandemics)
- Improved modelling capabilities, especially with respect to self-assembly
- Basic research should be supported in the area of engineering macromolecular and supramolecular structures.

Sustainable Chemistry Strategic Research Agenda 2005
The EU has established over thirty European Technology Platforms (ETPs) for topics of key importance to its citizens (33). Each of these is producing, or has produced, a Strategic Research Agenda (SRA). The Technology Platform for Sustainable Chemistry (SusChem) produced its SRA in 2005, which took a forward look to 2025, and identified strategically important issues (34). CEFIC has also produced a shorter booklet to publicise the SRA for Sustainable Chemistry to its members (35).

The European SRA contains contributions from four specific working groups: industrial biotechnology, material technologies, reaction and process design and horizontal issues. To present the reader with an accessible document, the detailed technical discussions have been prepared in the form of an appendix. It is clear that chemistry is a key driver for innovation in many technologies and disciplines, combining the benefits of traditional technologies with nano- and biotechnologies, leading to new and improved products. The three technology areas are covered in some detail, and are summarised below:

Industrial biotechnology
The approach looks at biotechnology processes and technologies for various sectors, including chemicals, food and nutrition, textiles, leather, animal feed, pulp and paper, energy and waste processing.

The main objectives for R&D are the development and production of novel, innovative products and processes in a cost- and eco-efficient manner, preferably using renewable raw materials, and the discovery and optimisation of micro-organism strains and biocatalysts. Biotechnology is already contributing to sustainable industrial development through:

- Reduced usage of water and traditional chemicals
- Reduced use of energy. Substitution of a number of chemical processes could make a significant contribution towards meeting the targets set by the Kyoto treaty
- Increased use of renewable resources, whether as chemical feedstock or fuels
- Production of new materials, by using cell cultures to make new pharmaceuticals and vaccines which could not otherwise be made
- Processing of biomass for bulk chemical applications including thermochemical and (catalytic) hydrothermal biomass conversion processes.

Materials technology
There is a focus on materials for mankind's future surroundings, which will be designed to enhance the quality of life. One important factor will be the role of nanoscience and the related nanotechnologies, in providing the knowledge necessary to lead to new innovative products and process methods. Nanotechnology is presented as an important enabling technology for the development of new material technologies. Interesting application areas are:

- Functional materials and biocompatible materials with tailored properties which include thin films and surface coatings, drug implant technologies and medical prosthetics using nanotechnological and biomimetic materials concepts
- Intelligent materials with tailored electrical (*e.g. super-conducting*),

optical and magnetic properties for applications in electronic devices such as displays or sensors, and for the support of quantum computing
- New sustainable technologies in the areas of both energy and environment, which include catalysis and renewable energy sources such as solar and fuel cell technologies
- New methods of polymerisation, including catalysis.

Modelling and self-assembly are identified as two of the most important research areas.

Reaction and process design
The developments necessary to achieve sustainable development are considered. Fundamental enabling technologies contribute to the entire life-cycle of processes ranging from product development, via catalyst and process development, plant development and operation, through to product handling and logistics. By integrating the approaches of chemical synthesis and process design and engineering, and providing key contributions to all relevant steps from reaction to viability of process plants, they can be applied to all areas of chemistry and biotechnology.

European Steel Technology Platform – Strategic Research Agenda
The EU has also produced an SRA for steel (36). Five working groups looking at profit, the automotive sector, the construction sectors, the planet and people were set up. Three proposed industrial programmes were forthcoming:

- Safe, clean, cost-effective and low capital intensive technologies
- Rational use of energy resources and residues management
- Attractive steel solutions for end users.

Protecting the environment from greenhouse gases and CO_2 emissions and increasing energy efficiency both constitute major issues for RTD programmes that are proposed; a third area is security and safety. Human resource issues, and especially skills and training are a major feature of the report.

Roadmap for the Canadian Aluminium Industry Technology

The publication of the Canadian Aluminium Industry Technology Roadmap in 2000 provided a positive approach and one of the achievements was the creation of the National Research Council's Aluminium Technology Centre. In 2006, it published an updated roadmap (37), with a view to combat the progressive leakage of finished product manufacturing to emerging economies. Canadian manufacturers were encouraged to invest in leading-edge design and manufacturing technologies rather defending maturing areas. Advanced modelling design techniques and fully-automated manufacturing, combined with a full awareness of the capabilities of aluminium is encouraged in order to gain customer acceptance and preference for aluminium.

Techniques for aluminium-joining need to be improved, and more respect for the environment and health of workers is also called for in the surface treatment industry. Surface treated alloys, with improved properties, are seen as an exciting area for development, in order to provide niche markets. The most important technical issues are:

* The development of new aluminium products having superior performance, produced using more efficient processes
* Better access to predictive and actual product performance testing facilities so as to meet the most demanding needs of the transportation, construction and energy industries.

A Technology Roadmap for the Canadian Welding and Joining Industry

In May 2006, Industry Canada produced another roadmap, this one for the welding and joining industry (38). Welding is a critical enabling technology for manufactured products, but senior executives often only see it as a commodity or expense, and in addition, its image to potential students is a dirty old-fashioned industry. The roadmap sets out to address the problems and identify priority project themes:

- Design and implement a funded, Canada-wide campaign directed at leaders in industry, government, education and the research
- Implement a funded manufacturing excellence and technology application program for the Canadian welding and joining industry
- Implement a funded comprehensive research innovation and advanced technology adoption program for welding and joining
- Implement a funded comprehensive education and training programme
- Implement a funded welding and joining Information Clearing House.

Materials powering Europe – MaterialsEuroRoads

MaterialsEuroRoads (39) is a forum for European key players in the field of foresight and forecast of developments in materials technology. MaterialsEuroRoads developed from the former Specific Support Action SMART, which was a roadmapping project within the EU's Sixth Framework Programme. Three roadmaps have been produced so far; the first being on energy, Materials Powering Europe, in April 2006. All three have also been collated in a book entitled *Future Perspectives of European Materials Research* (40). For Materials Powering Europe (41), the comments and research priorities for *Materials for Energy Efficiency* were as listed below.

- Innovative coatings technology is an essential way to improve efficiency, for stationary turbine components as well as rotating parts

- High temperature alloy development
- New battery storage materials are needed in order to improve storage
- Heat losses are currently far too high. Waste heat must be used much more efficiently
- Multi-scale modelling in materials technology should be progressed to reduce timescale from an idea to conception. A database to help this should be provided
- There is a great deal of scope to improve communications and networking between all interested parties. This would help inform governments. It would also enable transfer of information across the different sectors of the Energy Industry where some of the problems and issues are common
- The materials community working on materials topics in fossil plants should communicate with those in nuclear
- Emission free fossil fuel power plants are a requirement. Better public perception of the issues should be provided. Oxygen separation membranes and associated corrosion problems need to be addressed, and re-use of strategic materials and gas emissions should be undertaken
- A strategic plan for materials supply is needed, along with new materials concepts for energy storage
- Scale up / integration / implementation from laboratory to production of intelligent systems is required
- There is an identified need for new sealing and joining systems, with smart, reactive coatings
- Regulatory / fiscal incentives for the production of CO_2 free energy are imperative.

For *Materials for Sustainable Energy Technologies* comments and research priorities were as shown below.

- Mass production would be most beneficial to bringing the costs down for alternative sources of energy generation

- Better storage and transport of energy should be sought. It is recommended that improvements in superconductors and micro-turbines for distributed generation should be examined. In addition, advances in high energy density storage are needed
- Current funding is channelled towards 'political' topics; real issues that will help Europe should be followed, and less risk aversion would enable step leaps in progress
- The aim should be to produce materials that can withstand 2000°C, and other extreme conditions
- Costs are currently too high for new systems to be competitive. Functional materials that are highly efficient and are available on a large scale are a requirement. Coatings need to last much longer, and fuel-flexible plants should be explored
- There are few incentives for the provider, or user, of energy to change from current supplies. Energy legislation or tax concessions should be considered for the introduction of new ways of energy generation.

Materials for a Better Life – MaterialsEuroRoads
The Materials for Better Life report was issued in October 2006, and focused on three areas; biomaterials, packaging, and technical textiles (42). The priorities were identified as below.

Biomaterials
- Targeted drug therapy with controlled dosing
- Smart diagnostics
- Self diagnostic materials, and self monitoring
- Self healing materials
- Improve current implant materials
- Neurosensor prostheses
- Anti-microbial surfaces
- Chemical and structural biomimetics
- Smart surgical tools

- Improved biocompatibility – surface / interface science
- Nanotechnology developments that affect biomaterials
- Functional textiles
- Develop and refine bio-resorbable and bioactive materials
- General aids for the ageing population not just with biomaterials.

Packaging
- Develop high margin niche products
- Smart technology applications e.g. track and trace
- Zero waste society – emphasis on minimising or eliminating waste
- Application of nanotechnology for aesthetic coatings, barrier coatings, anti-microbial coatings, light weighting
- Novel adhesives with variable and controlled peel properties
- Lighter weight materials, including acoustic and thermal insulation
- Thin film / surface engineering
- Engineering of polymer structures and surfaces
- Ink and printing technologies
- Development of smart materials generally.

Technical textiles
- Develop high margin niche products
- Anti-allergy, anti-microbial finishes / fibres
- Improved cleaning – soil release and non-stain
- Thermal storage
- Smart technology applications – biotechnology, nanotechnology, integrated electronics
- Use of military developments elsewhere
- Actuators
- Impartial evaluation of existing floor covering materials – microbial and dust mite issues
- Flexible logic circuits

- Sensors
- New materials
- Improved backing materials.

Materials for a Safe Europe – MaterialsEuroRoads

A roadmap for Materials for a Safe Europe was also issued in October 2006 (43), and priorities were recorded under the following headings.

Cross-sectoral issues
- Focus on nanotechnological and biological sensors
- More interdisciplinarity
- Copy nature's protection and defence
- Provide more focus on major threats
- More simulation work required
- Establish standards for sensors
- Better communication of the benefits of sensors
- Better coordination and dissemination of activities in sensors.

Personal protection
- Thermochromic windows
- Pressure sensitive carpets
- Functionalised polymers as recognition
- Super-hydrophobic surfaces
- Conductive fibres
- Doped optical fibres
- Wearable body protection (military, ageing, leisure) – lighter weight and less obtrusive
- More effort into terahertz monitoring
- Artificial nose developments
- Sensing low concentrations of toxic agents and biohazards (explosives, radiation, food / water contamination, weapons)
- Advanced construction (reinforced composite concrete) and power supply

- Rapid and preferably miniaturised DNA screening methods
- Rapid eye / fingerprint screening
- New 'coded' materials for 'track and trace' (quantum dots, holograms)
- Tamper-proof packaging
- Portable and rapid analytical equipment for on-site analysis.

Roadmap of the European Platform for Advanced Engineering Materials and Technologies

This roadmap was produced as part of the Technology Platform's Strategic Research Agenda in June 2006 (44). It is a huge document that starts by stating what the three pillars of Advanced Engineering Materials Technologies are:

1. multifunctional materials
2. materials for extreme conditions
3. hybrid and multi-materials.

as used in engineering, and / or used to enhance the engineering products, systems and processes in areas such as energy, gas and oil, chemical, space, transportation, electronics, environment, health, etc.
Major challenges have been identified in the following areas:

- development of new cost-effective and environment-friendly materials and related processes for challenging application conditions
- condition assessment and performance / degradation modelling / prediction
- knowledge management and materials information delivery.

There is considerable detail on the challenges and research needs for different aspect of materials.

Manufuture – Strategic Research Agenda

The EU's Manufuture Technology Platform, aimed at assuring the future of manufacturing in Europe, produced a Strategic Research Agenda in September 2006, which may be obtained free of charge from their web site (45). The SRA identifies the key drivers as:

- competition, especially from emerging economies
- shortening life cycle of enabling technologies
- environmental and sustainability issues
- socio-economic environment
- regulatory climate
- values and public acceptance.

In response, the following, and their enabling technologies, are required.

- New, high added-value products and services
- New business models
- New manufacturing engineering
- Emerging manufacturing science and technologies
- Transformation of existing RTD and educational infrastructures to support world-class manufacturing, fostering researcher mobility, multidisciplinarity and lifelong learning.

Roadmap for MNT Gas Sensors

In December 2006, the Micro Nano Technology Network in the UK published a roadmap on the likely impact of nanotechnology in the field of gas sensors (46). This roadmap has now been incorporated into the activities of the Sensors KTN. The social benefits of gas sensors are to:

- provide early diagnostics in healthcare
- monitor complex processes that ensure a sustainable economy

79

- monitor and reducing pollutants in the environment
- provide early detection and forensic analysis for security
- reduce pollution by improving efficiency in transport.

Priority technologies include separation science, electronic components, optical light sources, nanomaterials, low cost/ integrated optics, microelectromechanical systems (MEMs), MEMs/ CMOS integration and electrochemical cells. Specific MNT priorities are as listed.

Nanomaterials
- Functionalised materials for gas filtration and separation
- Reproducible manufacture of carbon nanotubes, quantum dots and nanostructured metal oxides for improved gas sensitivity and selectivity.

Microfabrication
- High temperature amplifiers and logic for extreme environments
- Silicon MEMS integrated optics as a generic platform to address several niche markets, migrating telecoms manufacturing to small-run gas sensors
- Broad spectrum MEMS to discriminate compounds: micro mass spectrometry, ion mobility spectrometry and gas chromatography
- Establish credible production of new mid-IR light sources.

Grand research challenges
- VOC characterisation against complex backgrounds (e.g. BTEX, landfill, indoor and cabin air quality)
- Identification of normal and abnormal variations in gaseous markers of disease in breath and gut gases
- Improved selectivity and stability for semiconductor and nanomaterial gas sensors
- Combinatorial methodology for optimising sensing materials

- Integrated MEMS using combinatorial sensing arrays with widespread applicability
- Room temperature mid-IR and far-UV low cost, tunable light sources
- Detector for specific precursors and sources of asthma in the home.

Roadmap for Sustainable Technologies

The Chemistry Innovation Knowledge Transfer Network in the UK produced a Sustainable Technologies Roadmap in 2007 (47). They point out some areas where specific focus and activity would have the greatest impact on the development of a sustainable chemical industry in the UK:

Exploiting Existing Technologies

The experts involved in developing the roadmap identified many technologies that could be implemented today to help the development of a more sustainable chemical industry. This is particularly true in the areas of modelling and process design. A high priority activity should be helping industry to evaluate and implement known technologies that will reduce environmental impact and improve economic performance.

Developing Complete Packages for Industry

Much of the chemical industry lacks the resources and expertise to properly evaluate sustainable chemical technology options. Mobile demonstrator facilities are needed that will allow industry to try out real processes on site. Scale up is a key issue and the information and models to develop and cost a design are a critical part of the package. Industry also needs to be able to integrate the new process into their business models and financial planning. Providing good data and models plays an important part in encouraging the take up of new technology.

Demonstrating the Business Case

For most of the chemical industry, sustainable chemical technology is not successfully making the case that it will be a more profitable way to work. Sustainable chemical technology needs to win its place on the business agenda as a tool for improved competitiveness.

Green Product Design for the Chemical Industry
The chemical industry needs to develop its own model of green product design that is appropriate to the types of products, their typical risks, hazards and impacts.

Technology Roadmap - Applications of Nanotechnology in the Paper Industry

The objective of this Finnish technology roadmap (48), produced in February 2007, was to gather information and knowledge about applications of nanotechnology in the paper industry, and serves to make decisions regarding the future direction of the paper-related applied research at the Nanoscience Centre (NSC) of the University of Jyväskylä.

The research topics chosen by the experts are shown in Figure 3.2.

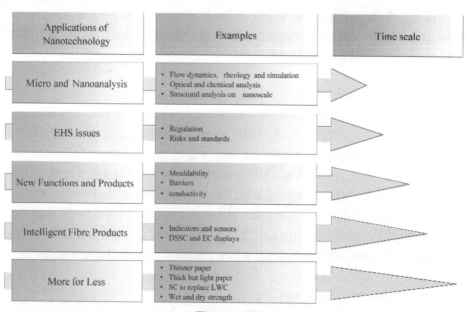

Figure 3.2

Technology Roadmap for Nano-Metrology

The UK's MNT (Micro Nanotechnology Network) produced a roadmap in September 2004 and this was updated by CEMMNT, the Centre of Excellence in Metrology for Micro and Nano Technologies, in April 2007. Both are now available from CEMMNT (49). The objective is to make the UK a leading centre for nano-metrology, where metrology is built-in at the design and process stages of nanotechnology developments and products. 'Wet' domains present particular challenges for nano-metrology techniques, and there is also an increasing demand to characterise, measure, and visualise in three dimensions at both the micro and nano-scales. Furthermore there is a continuing requirement for improved understanding of nano-scale interactions, which needs to be supported with more fundamental work in that area.

Awareness of the benefits of metrology was discussed and proposals made to encourage schools, universities and industry to become more active in the field through an active network.

Roadmap for Manutex Research

The EU's Joint Research Initiative for the Future of the European Textile, Clothing and Machinery Industries produced a roadmap (50) in May 2007. The main objective of the initiative is the establishment of a permanent collaboration forum between textile/ clothing manufacturers and developers, and manufacturers of machines, systems and tools for textile / clothing production, so that they can exchange information on major technological trends and evolving user needs.

A European Roadmap for Photonics and Nanotechnologies

A major component of the MONA (Merging Optics and Nanotechnology) Roadmap (51), published in 2008, is the identification of the highest priority economic growth areas, taking into account market size, market growth, and the positioning of European industry and research in these areas.

Highlights of the MONA Roadmap are:

• Nanophotonics benefits for 9 key applications

83

- Nanomaterials challenges and impact
- The most important nanophotonic devices
- Recommendations for European science and industry
- Custom-made roadmapping methodology
- 10-year roadmap for 12 key nanomaterials
- 10-year roadmap for 9 key types of equipment and processes
- 10-year roadmap on 9 key applications and related markets.

The materials aspects of the roadmap deal with material synthesis and material analysis. The materials under consideration are:

- quantum dots and wires in silicon, III-V, and II-VI materials
- plasmonics in metallic nanostructures
- high index-contrast nanostructures in silicon, and III-V materials
- microstructured fibres
- organic nanostructures
- carbon nanotubes
- integration of electronics and photonics
- nanoparticles in glass or polymer
- left-handed meta-materials.

Micro and Nanomanufacturing Strategic Research Agenda

In January 2008, a Strategic Research Agenda has been produced by the European Technology Platform for Micro- and Nanomanufacturing, MINAM (52). It addresses several key areas: manufacturing of nanomaterials, processing of nanosurfaces, micromanufacturing processes and integrated systems and platforms for micro- and nanomanufacturing.

The targets of the European micro- and nanomanufacturing industry are to:

- establish a new industry for the manufacturing of products

based on emerging micro- and nanotechnologies
- develop Europe as the leading location for the production of nanoparticles, micro- and nanostructures and components with "micro/nano inside"
- establish the complete value chain leading to the manufacturing of European micro- and nanotechnology products
- ensure that the new micro- and nanoproducts are produced at European facilities using equipment and systems of European origin thus overcoming the current situation in which only R&D, pilot cases and first production lines are set in Europe.

The outlined trends and research and development priorities are illustrated with examples from key industrial sectors in Europe. For example, the report details all the methods currently available for manufacturing nanomaterials, and compares sol-gel and plasma production in 2007 and their likely development up to 2013. Functionalisation of nanoparticles is then considered, along with their incorporation into materials.

Another section deals with manufacturing nanosurfaces, describing how nanoscale features can be obtained, and the properties that nano-engineered surfaces can achieve. A further section is on manufacturing of microcomponents, and finally integrated micro- and nanomanufacturing systems and platforms are presented, along with industrial sector examples.

In many ways this SRA is more of a review than a typical roadmap, but nevertheless the report contains a great deal of interesting and useful information.

REFERENCES

Some of the roadmaps referenced here may be obtained in hard copy from the organisations producing them, but the easiest way to access them is through the web references, which are given below. Should hard copies be required, then they can be printed off, or these same references may help with providing the right contacts to approach for paper copies. However, as time progresses, web sites go through changes, so some of the references may fall out of date. In these cases, it is suggested that the title of the roadmap is fed into a search engine, to determine if the roadmap is still available.

1   US Chemical Industry Vision 2020 exercise
    http://membership.acs.org/i/iec/docs/chemvision2020.pdf
2   US Chemical Industry Vision 2020 exercise focus on Computaional Fluid Dynamics
    http://www.chemicalvision2020.org/pdfs/compfluid.pdf
3   exercise with focus on green chemistry
    http://www.chemicalvision2020.org/pdfs/alternative_roadmap.pdf
4   US Chemical Industry Vision 2020 for computational chemistry
    http://www.chemicalvision2020.org/pdfs/compchem.pdf
5   US Chemical Industry Vision 2020 for separation technologies
    http://www.chemicalvision2020.org/pdfs/sepmap.pdf
6   Sandia National Laboratories roadmap for coatings on glass
    http://www.ca.sandia.gov/CRF/03_Reports/04_GlassCoatings/GlsCoatRptweb.pdf
7   Roadmap produced by petroleum industry leaders
    http://eelndom1.ee.doe.gov/oit/oitpdf.nsf/Files/petroleum.pdf/$file/petroleum.pdf
8   Industry Canada roadmap on metalcasting
    http://www.ic.gc.ca/epic/site/trm-crt.nsf/vwapj/metalcasting-fonderie_eng.pdf/$FILE/metalcasting-fonderie_eng.pdf
9   US Chemical Industry Vision 2020 exercise for the materials sector
    http://www.chemicalvision2020.org/pdfs/materials_tech_roadmap.pdf
10 US Advanced Ceramic Association's technology roadmap for advanced ceramics
    http://www.advancedceramics.org/ceramics_roadmap.pdf
11 US Chemical Industry Vision 2020 for biocatalysis
    http://www.chemicalvision2020.org/pdfs/biocatalysis.pdf
12 US Chemical Industry Vision 2020 for new process chemistry
    http://www.chemicalvision2020.org/pdfs/new_chemistry_roadmap.pdf
13 US Chemical Industry Vision 2020 for combinatorial methods
    http://campus.mst.edu/iac/iof/industies/CHEM/resources/combchemistry.pdf
14 Reaction engineering roadmap from the Centre for Waste Reduction

Technologies of AIChE
http://www.chemicalvision2020.org/pdfs/reaction_roadmap.pdf

15   US Department of Energy roadmap for aluminium
     http://www1.eere.energy.gov/industry/aluminum/pdfs/alumina.pdf

16   US roadmap for powder metallurgy and particulate materials
     http://www1.eere.energy.gov/industry/supporting_industries/pdfs/
     pmroadmapfinal.pdf

17   US Glass Manufacturing Industry Council's industry roadmap
     http://www1.eere.energy.gov/industry/glass/pdfs/
     glass2002roadmap.pdf

18   Roadmap on Immobilisation in Catalysis by the BHR Group
     http://www.bhrgroup.co.uk/extras/immocat.pdf

19   US Chemical Industry Vision 2020 for process equipment materials
     technology
     http://www.chemicalvision2020.org/pdfs/mti_roadmap.pdf

20   Roadmap from the steel industry in North America
     http://www1.eere.energy.gov/industry/steel/roadmap.html

21   Update of roadmap from reference 20
     http://www.steel.org/AM/Template.cfm?Section=Public_Policy&
     TEMPLATE=/CM/ContentDisplay.cfm&CONTENTID=4562

22   UK's Institute of Materials, Minerals and Mining roadmap for the rubber
     industry
     http://www.iom3.org/divisions/plastics_rubber/news_files/
     rubber_tech_roadmap.PDF

23   US Chemical Industry Vision 2020 roadmap covering Nanomaterials by
     Design
     http://www.chemicalvision2020.org/pdfs/nano_roadmap.pdf

24   UK's Powdermatrix Faraday Partnership roadmap in advanced ceramics
     http://217.118.138.78/powdermatrix/Ceramics_Roadmap_Dec04.pdf

25   UK's Powdermatrix Faraday Partnership roadmap for hardmetals
     http://217.118.138.78/powdermatrix/Hardmetals_Roadmap_Dec04.pdf

26   UK's Powdermatrix Faraday Partnership roadmap for the magnetic sector
     http://217.118.138.78/powdermatrix/Magnetic_Roadmap_Dec04.pdf

27   UK's Powdermatrix Faraday Partnership roadmap for the powder metals
     sector
     http://217.118.138.78/powdermatrix/Powder_Metals_Roadmap_Dec04.pdf

28   UK's Crystal Faraday Partnership roadmap for green chemical technology
     http://www.chemistryinnovation.co.uk/roadmap/sustainable/files/
     39014_1581448/2004Roadmap.pdf

29   UK's Impact Faraday Partnership roadmap for colloid and interface science
     http://www.new-game-plan.co.uk/Papers/Impact_Roadmap.pdf

30   UK's Insight Faraday Partnership roadmap for high throughput
      technologies
      http://amf.globalwatchonline.com/epicentric_portal/site/Innovation/
31   EU's Nanoroads initiative for aspects of nanomaterials
      http://www.nanoroadmap.it/
32   British Standards Institute's *Vocabulary for Nanoparticles*
      http://www.bsi-global.com/en/Standards-and-Publications/Industry-
      Sectors/Nanotechnologies/PAS-71/
33   EU Technology Platforms
      http://cordis.europa.eu/technology-platforms/individual_en.html
34   EU SRA in sustainable chemistry
      http://www.suschem.org/content.php?_document[ID]=2049&pageId=3217
35   CEFIC summary of the EU's SRA for sustainable chemistry
      http://www.cefic-sustech.org/files/Publications/
      ETP_sustainable_chemistry.pdf
36   European Steel Technology Platform's roadmap
      ftp://ftp.cordis.europa.eu/pub/coal-steel-rtd/docs/events-infostp_full-
      report.pdf
37   Canadian Aluminium Industry Technology Roadmap from the National
      Research Council's Aluminium Technology Centre
      http://www.trans-al.com/Default.aspx?alias=www.trans-al.com/network
38   Industry Canada roadmap for the welding and joining industry
      http://www.ic.gc.ca/epic/site/trm-crt.nsf/vwapj/welding_joining-
      soudage_assemblage_eng.pdf/$FILE/welding_joining-soudage_
      assemblage_eng.pdf
39   European SMART Consortium for MaterialsEuroRoads
      http://www.smart-ssa.net/c3/index.php?index=19
40   Schumacher, G., S Preston, A., Smith, P., et al., *Future Perspectives of European
      Materials Research*, 2007, ISBN 978-3-89336-477-0
41   European SMART MaterialsEuroRoads Consortium roadmap for *Energy
      powering Europe*
      http://www.smart-ssa.net/datapool/page/9/Proceedings_Energy.pdf
42   European SMART MaterialsEuroRoads Consortium roadmap for *Materials
      for a Better Life*
      http://www.smart-ssa.net/datapool/page/9/Proceedings_BetterLife.pdf
43   European SMART MaterialsEuroRoads Consortium roadmap for *A Safe
      Europe*
      http://www.smart-ssa.net/datapool/page/9/Proceedings_Security.pdf
44   SRA from the European Platform for Advanced Engineering Materials
      Technologies
      http://www.eumat.org/

45   SRA on the future of manufacturing from the European Manufuture
     Platform
     http://www.manufuture.org/SRA_form.html
46   UK's Sensors KTN's gas sensors roadmap
     http://www.technologyprogramme.org.uk/site/TechnologyReports/
     Gas%20Sensor%20Roadmap.pdf
47   UK Chemistry Innovation Knowledge Transfer Network's Sustainable
     Technologies Roadmap
     http://www.chemistryinnovation.co.uk/roadmap/sustainable/
     roadmap.asp?id=10
48   A Finnish technology roadmap on nanotechnology in their paper industry
     http://www.jyu.fi/science/muut_yksikot/nsc/en/pdf/nanopap
49   Centre of Excellence in Metrology for Micro and Nano Technologies's
     roadmap for nano-metrology
     http://www.cemmnt.co.uk/casestudies.php
50   Roadmap for the EU's Joint Research Initiative for the Future of the
     European Textile, Clothing and Machinery Industries
     http://www.manufuture.org/documents/manutex-def1.pdf
51   The Merging Optics and Nanotechnology group in Europe has produced a
     roadmap for photonics and nanotechnologies
     http://www.ist-mona.org/pdf/MONA_v13.pdf
52   SRA from the European Technology Platform for Micro- and
     Nanomanufacturing
     http://www.minamwebportal.eu/downloads/MINAMdocuments/
     2008-01-12%20-%20MINAM%20SRA%2012%2001%2008.pdf

CHAPTER 4

ROADMAPS IN MEDICINE AND HEALTHCARE

CONTENTS

BACKGROUND

With health and medical systems being such a key area for most nations, there are a number of roadmaps in this field, dealing with both general issues and specific topics.

ROADMAPS

Medical Imaging Technology Roadmap

In 2001, the vision for the Medical Imaging Technology Roadmap (1) was to improve patient care and enhance the global competitiveness of the Canadian medical sector, in an area where it is not a major player. Around the world, healthcare systems are under pressure to improve quality of care while containing or reducing costs. The roadmap comments on the challenge to reconcile these conflicting objectives which is complicated by an ageing population in the developed world, and by a wide differential in standards of care between developed and developing countries. Medical imaging has great potential to help resolve this dilemma, offering major advances in both diagnosis and precision image-guided therapy.

Following the use of x-rays, a number of new technologies for generating internal images of the human body have been developed, including CT (Computed Tomography); ultrasound; MRI (Magnetic Resonance Imaging); and nuclear imaging. In recent years the emphasis has moved to capturing, storing, and using images in digital form rather than in hardcopy form (film), and it is likely that this will continue. The medical imaging equipment business will see innovation and refinement in the present imaging processes, but new image generating technologies are not expected to capture a large market share.

The most significant areas of new business growth are likely to be in two areas of software or software-enhanced products:

- Products which facilitate the integration of medical

imaging into tele-health systems
- Products which enable or facilitate a variety of new image handling, image analysis and visualisation capabilities.

Medical Devices: The UK Industry and its Technology Development

In May 2003, the UK's Prime Faraday Partnership, which has now become part of the Knowledge Transfer Network for Electronics Enabled Products, published a report on medical devices (2). The report examines the UK's sector responsible for design and manufacture of medical devices and goes on to explore the current and future technological developments. A thorough review of the UK's status is given for the following areas.

- In vivo diagnostics
- Endoscopy and minimally invasive surgery
- Wound management
- Infusion devices
- Inhalation therapy
- Implantable devices
- Surgical devices
- Patient monitoring and patient-related instrumentation

Future activities in these areas are discussed.

Chemical Industry R&D Roadmap for Nanomaterials by Design

A roadmap, on Nanomaterials by Design, which is described in the Materials and Chemical Processes chapter (Chapter 3) was produced by the US Chemical Industry Vision 2020 Technology Partnership in December 2003 (3), and specifies key opportunities for nanomaterials in the medical and health sector; priority products and processes are:

- Nanosensors for early detection
- Nanomachines for therapy
- Sterilisation and control of superbugs in medical facilities

- Rapid DNA sequencing for diagnostics and therapeutics (DNA chips)
- Remote in vivo devices
- Drug delivery (miniaturisation, bio-arrays)
- Drug delivery - directed delivery of actives to target sites
- Prosthetics
- Tissue engineering (biocompatible, high performance materials)
- Diagnostic imaging
- Minimally invasive surgery.

Cancer Nanotechnology Plan
The US Department of Health and Human Services, through the National Institute of Health and the National Cancer Institute, produced a Cancer Nanotechnology Plan in July 2004 (4). The plan is spearheaded by the National Cancer Institute which acknowledges that *"nanotechnology offers the unprecedented and paradigm-changing opportunity to study and interact with normal and cancer cells in real time, at the molecular and cellular scales, and during the early stages of the cancer process"*. The vision statement acknowledges that nanotechnology will be the enabling technology for the following:

- Early imaging agents and diagnostics that will allow clinicians to detect cancer at its earliest, most easily treatable, pre-symptomatic stage
- Systems that will provide real-time assessments of therapeutic and surgical efficacy for accelerating clinical translation
- Multifunctional, targeted devices capable of bypassing biological barriers to deliver multiple therapeutic agents at high concentrations, with physiologically appropriate timing, directly to cancer cells and those tissues in the micro-environment that play a critical role in the growth and metastasis of cancer
- Agents capable of monitoring predictive molecular

changes and preventing precancerous cells from becoming
malignant
- Surveillance systems that will detect mutations that may
trigger the cancer process and genetic markers that indicate
a predisposition for cancer
- Novel methods for managing the symptoms of cancer that
adversely impact quality of life
- Research tools that will enable investigators to quickly
identify new targets for clinical development and predict
drug resistance.

The key opportunities for cancer nanotechnology which are
detailed in the report are:

- Molecular imaging and early detection
- In vivo imaging
- Reporters of efficacy
- Multifunctional therapeutics
- Prevention and control
- Research enablers.

MNT Network Roadmap in Diagnostics
The UK's Micro Nanotechnology Network carried out a Roadmap in
Diagnostics in March 2005. This was not published but focused on
making sure that the infrastructure was in place to maximise benefits
of this fragmented and diverse sector for the UK. Improved prototyping was seen as an essential requirement, and the need to enable
SMEs to have better access to market information and intellectual
property matters was identified. Better coordination of all activities
was also suggested to provide more opportunities in the UK.

European Technology Platform for Sustainable Chemistry – Materials Technology
In 2005, the European Technology Platform for Sustainable Chemistry
produced its Strategic Research Agenda (5) and prior to that had

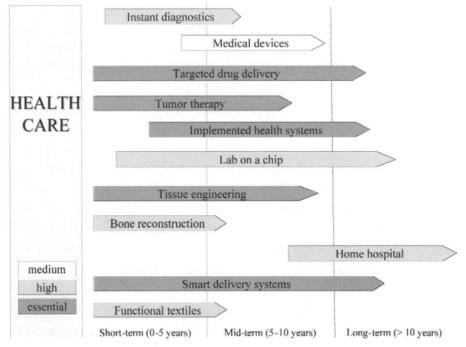

Figure 4.1

provided draft reports for each key area. The draft document for Materials Technology, which is no longer available on the web, showed a products roadmap for healthcare as shown in Figure 4.1.

The driver is increased life expectancy and the requirements are:

- Optimal and personalised medical care
- High demand for health prevention to reduce increasing medical costs
- New materials for implants
- Drug delivery
- Novel therapeutics
- Health protection and care
- Diagnostics and sensors for prevention and detection.

97

A key issue is the ability to reliably link biologically active molecules to surfaces, and this will give huge opportunities for improved medical devices and drug delivery strategies. Also important is the design of materials that mimic the behaviour of physiological systems such as muscle. There is strong emphasis on how nanochemistry will revolutionise healthcare and pharmaceuticals, with the potential for more efficient drug delivery and reduction of side effects.

Drug Encapsulation / Drug Delivery / Drug Targeting – EU Nanoroadmap Project

Under the Sixth Framework Programme (FP6), the European Commission instigated a number of roadmapping projects. Under 'Health and Medical Systems', four roadmaps were produced in November 2005 (6). Delivery and targeting of pharmaceutical, therapeutic and diagnostic agents is at the forefront of projects in nanomedicine. The report uses the term theranostics to describe integrated diagnosis and therapy, which will play an important role in the future. Identification of precise targets related to specific clinical conditions is crucial, so that required responses may be achieved while minimising side effects. Smart drug delivery systems are being developed which should protect the drug from decomposition during its journey to its target, and which then accumulate, actively or passively, within target tissue, and finally releasing the transported drug in a controlled time-dose profile.

The experts, in the Delphi process used for the roadmap, judged that to achieve their aims the following nanotechnology systems would be used:

- Inorganic nanoparticles – including for example calcium phosphate, gold, silicate, and magnetic particles
- Polymer nanoparticles – various natural or biocompatible synthetic polymers such as polysaccharides, polylactic acid, and polymers based on lactides, acetates, alkyl vinyl pyrrolidones, etc.
- Polymer therapeutics – molecular units with diameters of a few nanometres

- Nanocrystals – drugs ground down to nanoscale which are applied intraveneously as nanosuspensions
- Liposomes – small phospholipids bilayer vesicles.

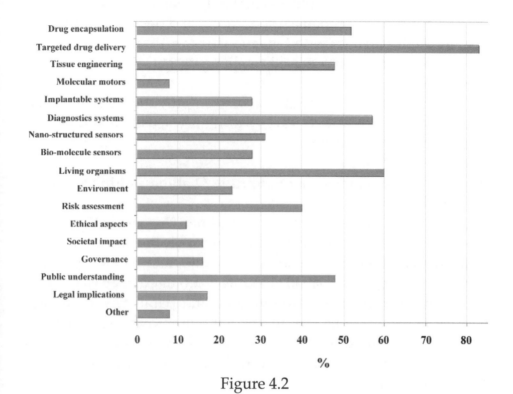

Figure 4.2

Overall for health and medical systems, the experts for all four roadmaps state that Europe should reinforce its activities in health and medical applications in the areas shown in Figure 4.2.

Molecular Imaging / Biophotonics / Medical Imaging - EU Nanoroadmap Project
The second roadmap in the EU Nanoroadmap Project was concerned mainly with imaging. Medical imaging is made up of all imaging technologies, and molecular imaging is the visual representation, characterisation, and quantification of biological processes at cellular

and sub-cellular levels within intact living organisms. Approaches should provide better methods for studying biological systems and for diagnosing and managing diseases.

Biophotonics uses light beams and other forms of energy to diagnose and monitor medical conditions, and one of the main technologies in this field is Photodynamic Therapy (PDT), in which drugs (e.g. photosensitizers) are used to eliminate pathogenic tissue in a specific manner.

Nanoparticulate materials are seen as providing modular platforms, from which a wide variety of highly sensitive and specific imaging agents can be created.

Biochips / High Throughput Screening / Lab-on-a-chip Devices – EU Nanoroadmap Project

The third roadmap in the EU Nanoroadmap Project for Health and Medical Systems was concerned mainly with Biochips, which are measurement devices, combining electronics and biology, for diagnosis. They require very small amounts of biological material, and by means of miniaturisation, automation, and parallelisation a large number of tests may be rapidly carried out on many samples. It is expected that nanotechnology will have a high impact in gene identification and gene sequencing, providing more sensitive, selective and accurate sensors.

Identification of suitable drugs will also be accelerated through the impact of nanotechnology, as will assay development and any high throughput screening. In addition, these new techniques will have a beneficial effect on food production and safety, as well as forensic medicine.

The use of nanotechnology in this area for medical diagnostics, point-of-care, predictive medicine, theranostics, therapy monitoring, and toxicology screening is considered.

Biomolecular Sensors – EU Nanoroadmap Project

The fourth roadmap in the EU Nanoroadmap Project series for Health and Medical Systems was on Biomolecular Sensors. Biosensors are analytical devices which convert biological responses into electrical signals, acting in a similar way to noses by specifically detecting certain molecules with recognition units that are based on biological components. The biologically responsive material is usually based on proteins such as enzymes or nucleic acid, but cells can also be used.

The experts for the roadmap said that the nanotechnologies that will make an impact in biosensors will be thin films, layers and surfaces, as well as nanoparticles, biopolymers, carbon nanotubes, nanoporous materials and molecular imaging.

Some of the challenges to be addressed are identified in the following list.

- Stability of bio-components is an issue (other than for glucose monitoring)
- Difficulty in integrating the different enabling components to achieve high sensitivity and selectivity
- Sensors capable of fast and automatic multi-analyte detection in clinical laboratories and home self-diagnostics
- Integration, intelligence to integrate data, minimally invasive methods, and reduction of collateral interactions with biomaterials
- Stability of the sensing element
- Linking sensor technologies to medical information technologies to improve diagnostics and theranostics
- Going to on-line detection in biofluids, increasing the number and specificity of markers for diseases, deducing the detection limit, and increasing reliability.

NIH Roadmap for Medical Research

During 2006, the National Institutes of Health (NIH) in the US solicited ideas for new initiatives from its stakeholders to identify cross-cutting challenges in biomedical research that would meet special criteria established for Common Fund (Roadmap) initiatives (7). In 2007, four topics were chosen to move forward as major roadmap initiatives:

1   Microbiome – the goal of the Human Microbiome Project is
    to characterise the microbial content of sites in the human
    body and examine whether changes in the microbiome can
    be related to diseases
2   Epigenetics – the study of stable genetic modifications that
    result in changes in gene expression and function without a
    corresponding alteration in DNA sequence. Epigenetics
    changes have been linked to disease, but further progress is
    required to obtain a better understanding
3   Protein capture tools / proteome tools – the proteome is
    the complete set of proteins in the body, and the project
    would allow characterisation of protein function in health
    and disease
4   Phenotyping services and tools – a human phenotype is the
    total physical appearance and constitution of a person.

One NIH roadmap pilot study will also be supported on a
Genetic Connectivity Map to discover and demonstrate the linkages
between diseases, drug candidates, and genetic manipulation.
Roadmap Coordination Groups are also assessing current efforts in
the following areas:

- Regenerative medicine - tissue engineering
- Pharmacogenomics – applying the power of genomics to
  the prediction of individual responses to medication
- Bioinformatics – applying principles of information
  sciences and technologies to make the diverse and complex
  life sciences data more understandable and useful.

The Canadian Biopharmaceutical Industry Technology Roadmap
In 2006, the Canadian Biopharmaceutical Technology Roadmap (8)
was issued with a view to maintaining Canada's world leadership
interests in areas of genomics, proteomics, regenerative medicine,
nanobiotechnology, and novel plant molecular manufacturing. The
roadmap sets out to ensure that a satisfactory infrastructure is in place

to counteract the commersialisation problem of premature birth of promising companies. Key recommendations are:

- Research spin-off companies should be enabled to build up their management teams, intellectual property positions and proofs of concept before advancing to private markets
- University industry liaison offices should be encouraged to devote resources to readying companies for approaching capital markets
- Despite some positive changes in the immigration rules, a great deal needs to be done both in immigration and taxation if Canada is to succeed in attracting supremely capable international managers here to pilot Canadian companies.

The report benchmarks Canada's expertise relative to the rest of the world in considerable detail, and the stakeholders list the important technologies as:

- Genomics - includes gene chips, micro arrays, expression analysis
- Proteomics - studies of protein identity, interactions, 2D gels
- Bioinformatics - gene and database mining, DNA profiling
- Metabolomics - metabolic profiling, drug effects
- Pharmacogenomics - individual response to drugs and disease, personalized medicines or treatment
- *In silico* Biology - modelling of drug effects and interactions
- Nanotechnologies - miniaturised or molecule-sized technologies
- Stem Cell Technologies - tissue- and cell-based regeneration
- Photodynamic Technologies - light-activated processes
- Combinatorial Chemistry - small molecule new drug libraries; rational drug design

- High-throughput Screening - technologies for candidate assessment and drug or lead discovery
- Monoclonal Antibodies - human antibodies, vaccines, products
- Manufacturing Technologies - protein production, fermentation, cell culture, molecular farming or access to GMP facilities
- Drug Delivery Technologies - new methods for drug delivery
- Biosensors - bio-based sensing of drugs, effects, efficacy

Roadmapping for Medical Devices

Malcolm Wilkinson of Technology for Industry Ltd published an article in 2006 entitled 'Roadmapping for Medical Devices' (9). It gives a brief background to roadmapping and illustrates it with a roadmap for drug delivery (which is not referenced) that is reproduced in Figure 4.3.

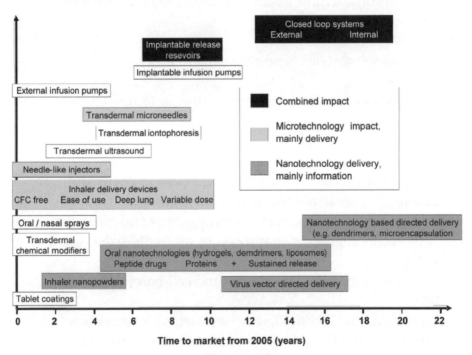

Figure 4.3

The Innovative Medicines Initiative – Strategic Research Agenda
In September 2006, the EU's Innovative Medicines Initiative produced a Strategic Research Agenda (10), in order to create biomedical R&D leadership for Europe to benefit patients and society. The principle causes of delay or bottlenecks in the current biomedical R&D process will be addressed. These bottlenecks have been identified as below.

- Predictivity of Safety Evaluation - creation of a European Centre of Drug Safety Research, and establishing a framework to develop biomarkers that will have human relevance and regulatory utility.
- Predictivity of Efficacy Evaluation - creating disease-specific European Imaging Networks, developing regional centres of excellence, creating disease-specific European centres for the validation of new biomarkers and enhancing collaborations with patients and regulatory authorities.
- Knowledge Management - establishing a Translational Knowledge Management team and creating a Knowledge Management Platform to develop effective data integration and analysis tools.
- Education and Training - establishing a European Medicines Research Academy, and the implementation of multi-disciplinary programmes to develop skills in integrating biology and medicine expertise.

Biomedical Technology Roadmap
A Biomedical Technology Roadmap was produced in September 2006 by the National Metals Technology Centre, NAMTEC, in the UK (11). Emphasis was on surface engineering, and especially metal-based products. The vision is to repair rather than replace; prevent in preference to cure. This will require early diagnosis, through scanners and ultrasound monitoring, and regular health checks would reduce the need for implants. Improved repair technologies are needed through research and development of biological and artificial materials that have gone through clinical trials.

Nanotechnology surface engineering developments should be adopted using improved methodologies; and tissue replication through improved simulation techniques is required. Future direction should be as follows:

- there needs to be better communication and technology transfer in this field
- need elimination of the hype and bad publicity through successful case studies, and professional publicity
- require substrate improvement through better integration with cell growth and use of smart biomimetic surfaces
- technologies to improve instrumentation for implants, using electromechanical devices for smaller interventions and inter-operative information.

There is a lack of development of new materials, because of a fear of litigation, and in addition, increasing regulatory issues are inhibiting progress.

Nanomedicine – Nanotechnology for Health
In November 2006, the European Technology Platform produced a Strategic Research Agenda for Nanomedicine (12). Nanomedicine is defined as the application of nanotechnology to achieve breakthroughs in healthcare. This will have an impact on all the stages of healthcare: preventive medicine, diagnosis, therapy, and follow-up care.

The promise nanomedicine holds is earlier detection of diseases and novel therapies which minimise discomfort for the patient, and hence provide cost savings all round. The report sets priorities based on a number of parameters:

- mortality rate
- level of suffering
- burden on society
- prevalence of the disease

- ability of nanotechnology to diagnose and overcome illnesses.

The strategy is to attack the diseases which are the greatest burden on society first, and the analysis has identified the following.

- Cardiovascular diseases
- Cancer
- Musculoskeletal disorders
- Neurodegenerative diseases and psychiatric conditions
- Diabetes
- Bacterial and viral infections.

Strategic research priorities are laid out in tables covering diagnostics, targeted delivery, and regenerative medicine for 1-2 years, 3-5 years, and more than 5 years.

REFERENCES

Some of the roadmaps referenced here may be obtained in hard copy from the organisations producing them, but the easiest way to access them is through the web references, which are given below. Should hard copies be required, then they can be printed off, or these same references may help with providing the right contacts to approach for paper copies. However, as time progresses, web sites go through changes, so some of the references may fall out of date. In these cases, it is suggested that the title of the roadmap is fed into a search engine, to determine if the roadmap is still available.

1   Canadian medical sector technology roadmap for imaging
    http://www.ic.gc.ca/epic/site/mitr-crtim.nsf/en/Home
2   UK's Prime Faraday Partnership roadmap for medical devices
    http://www.electronicproductsktn.org.uk/technology-watch/sector-profiles/medical-devices-the-uk-industry-and-its-technology-development.php

3   US Chemical Industry Vision 2020 report on Nanomaterials by Design
     http://www.chemicalvision2020.org/pdfs/nano_roadmap.pdf
4   National Cancer Institute 's Cancer Nanotechnology Plan
     http://nano.cancer.gov/about_alliance/cancer_nanotechnology_plan.pdf
5   SRA from the EU's Sustainable Chemistry Technology Platform
     http://www.suschem.org/content.php?_document[ID]=2049&pageId=3217
6   EU's Nanoroads initiative for health and medical systems
     http://www.nanoroadmap.it/
7   NIH roadmap for medical research
     http://nihroadmap.nih.gov/
8   Canadian roadmap for biopharmaceutical industry
     http://www.ic.gc.ca/epic/site/trm-crt.nsf/vwapj/biopharmaceutical-
     biopharmaceutique_eng.pdf/$FILE/biopharmaceutical-biopharmaceutique_
     eng.pdf
9   http://www.devicelink.com/mdt/archive/06/06/014.html
10   SRA from the EU's Innovative Medicines Initiative
     http://www.imi-europe.org/DocStorage/PublicSiteAdmin/Publications/
     Strategic%20Research%20Agenda%20(Version%202).pdf
11   UK's National Metals Technology Centre roadmap on Biomedical
     Technology
     http://www.namtec.co.uk/uploads/docs/1187184150SEG_
     Biomed_Report.pdf
12   EU Technology Platform SRA for nanomedicine
     ftp://ftp.cordis.europa.eu/pub/nanotechnology/docs/
     nanomedicine_bat_en.pdf

CHAPTER 5

ROADMAPS IN THE TRANSPORT INDUSTRY

CONTENTS

BACKGROUND

As might be expected, there are more roadmaps for vehicles than any other form of transport, with the aerospace industry coming second. There are several European reports detailing general aspects of transport.

It is interesting to note that although most forms of transport have similar issues, the industry could benefit from more cross-fertilisation, especially in efforts associated with lighter weight materials, improved fuel efficiency, and recycling issues.

ROADMAPS

Canadian Aircraft Design, Manufacturing and Repair, and Overhaul – Technology Roadmap

This roadmap was produced for Canada in October 1996 by Ontario aircraft companies and research organisations in partnership with the National Research Council (1). It identifies critical enabling technologies which the sector will require in order to design, build and maintain aircraft, aircraft systems and components to meet customer requirements in the period 2001-2005, as well as identify and reach consensus on future technology requirements. Technologies are selected on the basis of their potential contribution to marketplace competitiveness and their strategic applicability across the industry sector. It describes fifty enabling technologies in eight technology areas (design, environmental issues, maintenance and repair, and overhaul, as well as management, manufacturing, materials and structures, systems, and visualisation), and is published in two volumes.

Aluminum Industry Roadmap for the Automotive Market: Enabling Technologies and Challenges for Body Structures and Closures

In May 1999, the American Aluminum Association produced a roadmap specifically for the automotive sector (2). It was a 'follow-

111

up' to their more general roadmap 'Aluminum Industry Technology Roadmap' produced in 1997 and then updated in February 2003 (3). The generic Aluminum Industry Technology Roadmap sets research goals in the production of primary aluminum and aluminum sheet and extrusions to improve process efficiency. The Aluminum Industry Roadmap for the Automotive Market discusses the research and development necessary to meet the technological challenges of casting, forming, joining, and recycling cost-effective aluminum components for the vehicles.

Good automotive design is also crucial to the successful use of aluminum in future vehicles. The challengers for the design engineer are to integrate the properties of lightweight materials, revolutionary forms for automotive components, unique manufacturing processes, and vehicle recyclability. At the same time, the designer can take advantage of the flexibility inherent in these new materials and processes to propose new vehicles that will appeal to the consumer. Aluminum is claimed to be the key to making these vehicles not only lightweight but also safe, fuel-efficient, environmentally compatible, and cost-effective.

A Roadmap for Recycling End-of-Life Vehicles of the Future

The US Department of Energy's Office of Advanced Automotive Technologies and the Argonne National Laboratory produced a roadmap in May 2001 for Recycling End-of-Life Vehicles of the Future (4). It defines recycling as:

> *"Any cost-effective use of parts, components or materials from an obsolete car that would otherwise be sent to landfill, including parts re-use and re-manufacturing, materials recovery for re-use in an original application or for use in any other viable application, and materials recovery for thermochemical conversion to fuels and/or chemicals".*

The top factors affecting automobile recycling for the next 20 years were listed as :

- Economic value of recovered material and components
- Material content of vehicles
- Competing vehicle design requirements
- Capability to separate and sort material
- Hazardous material and contamination
- Capital availability to build infrastructure
- Collection costs, transport costs, and materials supply
- Regulations impacting recycling
- Consumer opinion
- Unforeseen factors.

All of these factors are likely to be important for the recycling of any material in most industry sectors. For the automotive industry it is estimated that End-of-Life Vehicles (ELVs) in 2020 will be:

- 75% metal
- 15% plastic
- 10% other.

However, since the report was written in 2001, there has been the beginning of a trend to nanocomposite materials in cars with consequential reduction in weight, as well as to other light weight materials such as ultra-light steels and aluminium. Looking specifically at technology changes, it is likely that recycling will have a strong influence on the choice of materials and the ability to remove and separate them at the end of their life. The diversity and complexity of the materials used in vehicles presents a major challenge. Overall, the drivers are economic and regulatory ones, and the roadmap lists the priority needs for ELV recycling.

Plastics in Automotive Markets – Vision and Technology Roadmap
The American Plastics Council, working with the automotive industry, produced a roadmap in 2001 for the 'plastic car' (5). To achieve their vision, the automotive plastics industry proposed to pursue a business strategy defined by four elements:

- New Applications for Plastics
  - Develop a robust portfolio of polymer-based material options and related tools to make plastics the preferred material for automotive designers and manufacturers
  - Maximize the performance advantages of polymers and composites for conventional vehicle platforms
  - Design and prototype entirely new vehicle architectures that build on the unique material, design, and processing advantages of plastics
- Speed to Market
  - Shorten design, development, and engineering cycles to rapidly take new polymer-based applications from initial concept to commercial product
  - Provide reliable methods and tools to predict material performance over the entire life of the vehicle
  - Exploit opportunities to increase efficiency and value through out the automotive value chain by implementing new design tools, Internet-supported product development, innovative manufacturing processes, training initiatives, and e-commerce
- Enabling Infrastructure
  - Build a dynamic, plastics-based manufacturing and supply infrastructure that outperforms conventional systems
  - Develop robust manufacturing platforms that are rapid, agile, and less capital-intensive than competing options, and enable mass customisation of vehicles
  - Present automakers with a sound business case for plastics and demonstrate the competitive advantages of using plastics-intensive designs
  - Support new and expanded educational and training programs in academia and industry that expand the knowledge base in polymer science and engineering and strengthen the interface with automotive engineering needs
- Sustainable Transportation
  - Develop and use new plastics to create sustainable vehicle systems.

- Leverage the environmental advantages of polymer-based vehicles over their entire life cycle, including materials processing, vehicle production, vehicle use, and recycling.
- Promote polymer-based components where they offer distinct energy efficiency and other environmental advantages over existing components
- Develop innovative, sustainable technologies and infrastructures to recover and recycle plastics
- Strengthen education and outreach for students and consumers to improve understanding of the value of plastics in vehicles and help drive innovation.

Model Based Systems in Automotive Domains: Applications and Trends - Monet Roadmap

Monet is a European Centre of Excellence in 'artificial intelligence into industry', based at the University of Wales in Aberystwyth. It produced a report in June 2002 entitled Model Based Systems in Automotive Domains: Applications and Trends (6). The approach taken has been through questionnaires to experts in the field. It claims that model-based reasoning has proved to be a very powerful technology for automotive applications for tasks such as diagnosis, design, and simulation. The general idea is that qualitative models can support several activities which are critical to the life cycle of vehicles: from analysis of the original design through on-board monitoring, diagnosis and recovery, to diagnosis and repair in the workshop.

Technology Roadmap for Marine and Ocean Industry

This roadmap, which was issued in 2003 (7) and has been updated since then, addresses five areas, one of which is concerned with shipping:

1   Shipbuilding and industrial marine
2   Marine operations
3   Offshore oil and gas

115

4   Fisheries and aquaculture
5   Ocean Technology.

The overall vision is for the Canadian shipbuilding and industrial marine industry to make a strong recovery based on sustained domestic demand fuelled primarily by diverse fleet replacement needs and a designed and made-in-Canada Future Ship as well as success in related component manufacturing. The Canadian industry has expertise in Roll-on/Roll-off (RoRo) ferry and cargo ships and is gaining expertise in industrial marine. Opportunities for internal markets are a main driver with plans to provide a renewed Great Lakes Shipping fleet, replacement of Canadian Coastguard vessels, and with the Canadian Navy.

Future Road Vehicle Research – R&D Technology Roadmap
This roadmap (8) was produced in 2003 by FURORE, a project initiated by EARPA, the European Automotive Research Partners Association, and financed by the European Commission within the 5th Framework Programme. The consortium identified the following research targets:

Table 5.1

Fuels	2020: Achieve EU target 20% substitute fuel / combustion optimised together, significant depot-fuelled fleets (e.g. bus) using CNG and H_2 2030: Route map to sustainable transport identified and enacted
CO_2 / GHG	2020: Car: 95g/km, Truck: 20% on today, Bus: 40% on today 2030: Car: 80g/km
Emissions	2020: Car: 50% EU IV + PM 0.1 control, Truck & Bus: NO_x <25% EU IV, PM <50% EU IV, inclusion of unregulated compounds, local control 2030: Understanding of the true needs of local environment achieved
Safety	2020: Road deaths – 75% 2030-2050: Introduction of autonomous driving
Traffic	2020: Telematics and traffic management enable congestion and stress free highway driving
Noise	2020: Adequate noise level to the ambient. Holistic approach for real world noise reduction 2030-2050: Further reduction in urban noise towards WHO targets
Recycling	2020: 85%, introduction of useable cradle-to-grave analysis standard 2040: 95% by weight, low environmental impact of disposal of last 5%

For each of the above topics the report details the requirements that are envisaged. In summary:

- Research investment is necessary in the evolution of powertrain technology, based on IC-engines and conventional based fuels, thereby guaranteeing global competitiveness of European automotive industry together with reduced energy dependency and improved environment
- Research in completely new technologies is essential to promote sustainable advances in environment and energy security
- Importance of energy consumption measures needs to be regarded as very high, independent from future scenarios on propulsion systems or fuels
- A holistic system approach integrating specific and generic technologies as well as development tools and platforms will lead to better, faster and cheaper research results.

Plastics in Automotive Markets – Vision and Technology Roadmap
In April 2004, the American Plastics Council carried out a roadmap on the future of plastics in the automotive industry (9), which provided guidance to the automotive and plastics industries and their stakeholders as they pursue the research and development that is needed to create innovative materials and design approaches that meet automotive performance criteria. Automakers are faced with formidable challenges:

- Consumers expect cars to perform better, have more features, and cost less
- Existing architectures are reaching their practical limit
- Globalisation and rapid manufacturing techniques are driving the industry to faster innovation and development
- Design and assembly times must be compressed, and

117

tooling and fabrication costs minimised
- Expectations for a clean environment and sustainable products are pushing automakers to be more responsible in the use of energy and materials.

The vision is that by 2020 the automotive industry will have established plastics as a material of choice in the design of all major automotive components and systems.

- Plastics will be the preferred material for enhancing component and system value
- Designing with plastics and composites will positively impact vehicle cost, environmental performance, and customer preferences
- Plastics will be the principal tool to produce safer, more affordable, stylish, durable, energy-efficient, and low emission vehicles in every market segment
- Rapid, cost-effective processing systems will provide automakers with the flexibility to respond to dynamic markets
- Polymer-based architectures will give automakers the freedom to create innovative vehicles that increase the value throughout the supply chain and for the driving public.

To achieve the strategic goals and vision a diverse portfolio of critical technologies will be pursued. Critical new technology development areas are:

- Advanced material systems
- Predictive engineering
- Automotive design
- Advanced manufacturing technology
- Business, market, and education infrastructure
- Environmental performance.

Strategic Research Agenda for Aeronautics
The Advisory Council for Aeronautics Research in Europe (ACARE) produced a Strategic Research Agenda in October 2004 (10). The initial findings concluded that air transport is a significant contributor to European wealth. The resultant benefit is spread across all Member States, as a result of its direct contribution (2.6% GDP and 3 million jobs), and its total contribution to the economy is estimated to be in excess of 10% of GDP. European research needs more money, and re-analysis has shown that, taking an encompassing view of the research needed and the necessarily associated facilities and demonstrators, about 65% more funding is required over the 20 year forward view than is presently being invested. Concerns are also expressed about the need for more people because the industry will face a shortage of skilled young people in the future. Also, research needs to be more efficient across Europe, with better co-ordination and less duplication of work.

European Road Transport 2020: A Vision and Strategic Research Agenda
In December 2004, the European Road Transport Research Advisory Council (ERTRAC) published its Strategic Research Agenda (11). All road transport stakeholders were brought together in order to define the necessary research activities which would result in a better future, characterised by more efficient energy use, security of energy supply, better air quality and environment, enhanced safety and security, and easier mobility. This process provided the transport sector with the right framework so as to contribute to the EU's goal to become the most competitive and dynamic knowledge-based economy in the world, capable of sustainable economic growth with more and better jobs and greater social cohesion.

The future trends and challenges to achieve the vision for the year 2020 and beyond are presented under the four following themes:

- Mobility of people and transport of goods
- Safety and security

- Environment, energy and resources
- Design and production systems.

Under the section on 'cleaner, quieter and more energy efficient road transport system' the major aspects of the vision are recorded as:

- Efforts will continue to reduce greenhouse gas emissions and energy use from individual vehicles which have already been reduced due to a wider use of highly fuel-efficient vehicles and increasing use of improved conventional, renewable and alternative low carbon fuels
- Renewable and alternative low-carbon fuels together with advanced vehicle powertrains begin contributing to environmental improvement and security of energy supply.
- Emissions other than CO_2 from new road vehicles, including two-wheelers, over their entire life cycle are at levels that have negligible impact on air quality.
- Noise from the road traffic system has been reduced.
- Vehicle manufacturing systems and road construction and maintenance processes are designed to maximise the extent of recycling. Advanced technologies allow a substantially more efficient use of resources and energy.
- Road transport energy use and resources approach sustainable levels.
- Due to new cleaning and protection technologies, the impact from surface run-off on water quality is minimal.

New approaches to the road transport system are minimising environmental impacts on communities and natural habitats.

Roadmap for Foresight Vehicle Technology
As part of the UK Government's Foresight exercise, the Society of Motor Manufacturers and Traders Limited produced, in 2004, a Foresight Vehicle Technology Roadmap (12). Technology targets are shown in Table 5.2.

Table 5.2

	0-5 years	5-10 years	10-20 years
Safety	• Selection of joining systems to match material performance capabilities	• Design/production and validation of 'smart' crash structures	
Product configurability and flexibility	• Component integration • Easier separation of materials for recycling or re-use • Effect of modular structures (and joining) on crash structures/NVH /stiffness • Robust engineering solutions for rapid modular reconfiguration	• Automotive industry relevant materials information database with all needs covered one source • Management of customer customisation and effect on design process/homologation and supply chain	
Economics	• Reduce cost of moulded composites • Component performance beyond single vehicle life • Development costs • Re-processing of metal mixtures to give pure metals for re-use • A higher, safer and more environmentally sound vehicle development	• Disassembly techniques • Develop viable alternative to traditional paint finish for body panels	
Environment	• Establish standards of environmental friendliness • Development of polymer separation techniques • ELV compliant composite materials • Reduce vehicle weight • Attachment strategies for dismantling • Wider understanding of materials in the industry • Overcoming energy saving vs. recycling perceptions • National system for re-use of components • Low cost CFRP panels and structures	• New magnetic materials for hybrid/ fuel cell powertrain • Develop re-use mechanisms/ methodologies • Identify higher value markets for recovered materials • National systems for materials re-use and recycle	• Solve H_2 fuel infrastructure issues to enable widespread uptake and use • Hardwearing, low friction coatings to eliminate lubricants from powertrains
Manufacturing systems	• Joining hybrid structures • Surface quality thermoplastic composites • Develop low cost composite manufacturing	• Coatings which survive production • Reduce time to manufacture for novel technologies	• Die-less forming

121

	process
	• Cost effective
	  joining/dismantling of
	  mixed material structures
	• Cheap, environmentally
	  friendly system to join
	  steel, aluminium and
		• Materials that do not
		  require paint protection
		• Convergence of business
		  and technology research
		  models
		• Flat pack/modularity
		  requires ability to make	

	magnesium without
	corrosion issues
	• Awareness of and access
	  to process models and
	  life cycle analysis
	• Establish central register
	  of production routes to
	  advise on potential
	  facility sharing
	• Single piece structure
	  development costs
		cheaper, structural, sealed
		joints post-paint process	

Roadmap for Product Development Transition to Lean (PDTTL)

The Lean Aerospace Initiative (LAI) is a collaborative effort among major elements of the United States Air Force, leading companies within the aerospace defence industry, and the Massachusetts Institute of Technology. LAI was formed to identify and implement lean principles and practices throughout the military aerospace systems' acquisition, development, and production processes. Their web site refers to a number of roadmaps, and the Product Development Transition to Lean Roadmap was produced in March 2005 (13).

Technology Roadmap in Composites for the Automotive Industry

In October 2005, the UK's National Composite Network produced a technology roadmap for Composites in the Automotive Industry, which may be downloaded from their web site (14). It was concluded that although the UK is strong in the use of composites in niche areas of the automotive, aerospace and marine industries, all those sectors would benefit from more interaction. Other conclusions were:

• Thermoplastic composite structures have the potential to replace metal parts but more attention is needed for better processing and automation. There is also a gap in the integration of metals, thermosets, thermoplastics and other hybrids.

- Close attention needs to be given to the repair infrastructure, and the use of smart materials for damage assessment and correction.
- Recycling issues for composites need to be addressed, with issues such as identification, bonding and de-bonding, and re-use needing development work
- Need for improved competence in computer aided engineering, in 'crash', durability, and cost models.
- There is a skill gap in prototyping but not at graduate level.
- Government funding should be directed at:
  - Durability and performance
  - High speed, high volume processing with a large demonstrator facility
  - Crash prediction and repair
  - Recycling
  - Processing issues such as preforming straight to laminate, resin infrastructuring, and reduced cycle times.

Technology Roadmap in Composites for the Marine Industry
In March 2006, the UK's National Composite Network also produced a Technology Roadmap in Composites for the Marine Industry which may be downloaded free of charge from their web site (14). It was again concluded that there is a great deal of scope for the Marine Industry to use technology that is already developed for the Automotive and Aerospace Industries, making use of the nanocomposite and nanocoating materials that are now available. In addition, improved efficiencies within manufacturing are needed, looking at manufacturing in low cost centres, and moving to lean processing, with better communication between engineers and suppliers. Time availability and production pressures inhibit development of new technologies, so more focused effort towards development should be undertaken.

Roadmap Report Concerning the Use of Nanomaterials in the Automotive Sector

Within the European Sixth Framework Programme (FP6), a roadmap was produced (15) for Nanomaterials in the Automotive Sector, which focused on how the small and medium sized companies could benefit their product development. The main purpose was:

- To give an overview on relevant nanomaterials for industrial applications in the automotive sector at short, middle and long term
- To give the actual level of development of the nanomaterials and an approximate evolution of it in the short, middle and long term
- To be adapted to SMEs.

Nanomaterials are already making an impact and the report considers nanotechnology activities in the following domains of an automobile:

- Frames and body parts
- Engines and powertrain
- Paints and coatings
- Suspension and breaking systems
- Lubrication
- Tyres
- Exhaust systems and catalytic converters
- Electric and electronic equipment.

The report is an excellent review of what technologies are currently available. It also predicts developments in the area of nanomaterials applications in the transport sector, and discusses the advantages and disadvantages.

Strategic Research Agenda For Urban Mobility

Euroforum produced a Strategic Research Agenda for Urban Mobility in April 2006 (16), which addresses research issues in the particular field of urban transport, considering all transport modes and focusing on intermodality for both passenger and freight transport.

This Strategic Research Agenda is primarily structured around the four components of the urban mobility system. Two components cover transport demand:

- The users' needs and behaviour - the starting point of both passenger and freight transport
- The urban structure - land use, urban sprawl and the relationship with mobility and infrastructure.

Two other components are for transport supply:

- Integrated mobility services - services (often ICT-based, like travel information and payment services) that enable a dynamic interaction between demand and supply
- Integrated transport systems - the 'hardware' of the urban mobility system, such as road and rail infrastructure, and the operation of public and private road and rail vehicles.

Strategic Research Agenda – Waterborne Transport and Operations
In May 2006, The EU's Technology Platform for Transport produced a Strategic Research Agenda in Waterborne Transport and Operations (17). Key priorities for research, development and innovation are recorded under the following headings:

- Safe, sustainable and efficient waterborne operations
  - Implementing goal-based / risk-based frameworks for cost efficient safety
  - Zero accidents target
  - The 'crashworthy' vessel
  - Low emission vessels and waterborne activities
  - Enhanced waterborne security
- A competitive European maritime industry

125

- Innovative vessels and floating structures
- Innovative marine equipment and systems
- Tools for accelerated innovation
- Next generation production processes
- Effective waterborne operations
- Technologies for new and extended marine operations
- Manage and facilitate growth and changing trade patterns
- Accelerated development of new port and infrastructure facilities
- Inter-operability between modes
- More effective ports and infrastructure
- Intelligent transportation and integrated ICT solutions
- Understand environmental impact of infrastructure building and dredging
- Traffic management strategies.

The Strategic Research Agenda is particularly comprehensive and the full report is well illustrated.

Technology Roadmap in Composites for the Aerospace Industry
In June 2006, the UK's National Composite Network produced a third Technology Roadmap in Composites, this time for the Aerospace Industry. As with the others this may be downloaded free of charge from their web site (14).

The vision is to achieve:

- Leadership in design and development of aerospace composites, by:
  - Establishing clusters of excellence in composites
  - Training more good engineers with composite skills, and offering clearer career progression and structure to encourage engineers to stay technical
  - Funding demonstrator activities
  - Establish high profile application to increase awareness of composites

126

- Improved manufacturing situation through control of manufacturing in low cost areas of the world and investment in design of parts and processes for high value composites is required through automated production to increase quality and reduce costs in the UK.

Technology gaps were identified as:

- New materials for out-of-autoclave processing and for preforms are needed through effective partnerships between materials manufacturers and composite end users
- Creating effective partnerships for technology development. This could be achieved for the UK through clustering between academic experts and industry, as is the case in some countries. A database of capabilities should also be established
- More effort into manufacturing and process research, since it is not seen by academics as challenging
- Improved understanding of variability within manufacturing structures
- In addition the workshop identified a number of specific areas where technology was weak.

The Future of Automotive Research

The European Association of Automotive Suppliers (CLEPA) produced a roadmap entitled 'The Future of Automotive Research' in November 2006 (18). CLEPA represents 72 of the world's most prominent suppliers for car parts, systems and modules, and 20 national trade associations and European sectoral associations, which represent more than 3,000 companies, employing more than three million people, covering all products and services within the automotive supply chain.

Pre-competitive research is particularly important in this research area to ensure sustainable processes from initial design to end-of-life recycling of vehicles. Specifically, the development of intelligent materials is currently gaining ground with examples such as intelligent tyres, electrochromic rear mirrors and heat reflecting surfaces. CLEPA believes that focus should be placed on the following topics:

- Further developing the intelligent use of conventional and new materials and lubricants, specifically focusing on multi-functional and highly integrated components to reduce number and consumption of components
- The development of lighter materials and the intelligent combination of materials (composites)
- Reducing friction and reducing wear
- Nanotechnology and nanomaterials offer promising opportunities for the European automotive industry but the area calls for further pre-competitive research
- In terms of design and processing, the development of simulation technology is especially urgent and would benefit from joint European research under FP7
- To be able to remain competitive with economies of scale production while adapting to increasingly fragmented markets, component platforms that can produce several different car silhouettes and reduce the development time for a car is a priority which should be met with support in FP7.

Strategic Research Agenda for High Altitude Aircraft and Airship Remote Sensing Applications

The Specific Support Action of the European Union Sixth Framework Program has produced, in 2006, a Strategic Research Agenda for High Altitude Aircraft and Airship (HAAS) Sensing Applications (19). The report takes into account two main aspects, forest fire monitoring and mapping.

HAAS missions and applications have the potential to fill in the missing link between airborne and spaceborne missions, since they fly at high altitude but still much lower than satellites. The superior flexibility and the constant availability of the HAAS provides rapid remote sensing data and communication services at high update rates and over a specific target area. The sensor technologies are already on a high level of maturity, but need customised developments to meet the specific capabilities and the environment of HAAS platforms.

Basically the same sensors are required by a large number of observation missions, and high-bandwidth downlink is necessary to support data from multiple sensors. There is a need for standard data interfaces to allow easy integration in standard data processing and downlink systems. Implementation of on-board processing (data management, feature extraction, classification, filtering, encryption, data compression) should be investigated. In addition, standard payload bays should be available for fast and flexible change of payload modules. The platform should provide observation and communication capabilities at the same time, leading to the concept of HAAS as a multi-mission platform. One single platform can be equipped with several sensors and telecommunication payloads to provide different services at the same time or without the need of changing the payload. Bottlenecks for the use of HAAS for remote sensing and communication applications are mostly on the platform and not on the sensors.

Nanotechnology in Aerospace
The European Nanotechnology Gateway, Nanoforum.org, produced a report in February 2007 entitled 'Nanotechnology in Aerospace' (20), which gives a concise introduction and contribution on trends in nanomaterials and nanotechnologies for applications in the civil aeronautics and space sectors in Europe. Military R&D and applications were excluded.

There is a focus on carbon nanotube reinforced polymers, metallic materials and polymer nanocomposites. Carbon nanotube reinforced polymers are being researched for aerospace applications because of their good strength to weight ratio, flame and vibration resistance, antistatic and electrical properties. Nanometals are of interest for their hardness and suitability in hard coatings. The new nanometal production technology, Severe Plastic Deformation (SPD) promises higher strength, corrosion and wear resistance and other benefits compared to other metals. There are three relevant types of polymer nanocomposites:

- Layered silicate (clay)
- Nanofibre / carbon nanotube filled polymer composites
- High performance polymer nanocomposite resins.

The report reviews the current activities of nanotechnology in the aerospace industry, also looks at the impact of nanoelectronics on aeronautics. Requirements for future R&D for nanomaterials and nanotechnologies for aeronautics and spacecraft are discussed, and the focus is on gaps in current research and needs for technical performance of available materials and devices which are critical enablers of future aeronautic and space systems. Two general points were made; the first being the need to educate sufficient numbers of qualified scientists and engineers to work in R&D in this sector in Europe, and the lack of cooperation between companies and research organisations in aerospace and in nanotechnology.

These technical requirements for future aeronautics address quality and affordability, environment, security, safety and air transport efficiency. Relevant onboard nanotechnologies can be applied in airframes, propulsion, aircraft avionics, systems and equipment. Nanotechnology may be applied in aircraft some twenty years after the technologies have been validated for airworthiness, but new research needs for nanotechnology applications in space include nanomaterials for spacecraft structure and energy production and storage, including solar cells, fuel cells, batteries and accumulators and capacitors. Other nanotechnology research needs are in data storage, processing and transmission, life support systems, and nanomaterials and thin films for spacecraft.

Visionary applications of nanotechnology in space include molecular nanotechnology and electronics for space, the space elevator, nano and pico satellites, the gossamer spacecraft and space solar power.

REFERENCES

Some of the roadmaps referenced here may be obtained in hard copy from the organisations producing them, but the easiest way to access them is through the web references, which are given below. Should hard copies be required, then they can be printed off, or these same references may help with providing the right contacts to approach for paper copies. However, as time progresses, web sites go through changes, so some of the references may fall out of date. In these cases, it is suggested that the title of the roadmap is fed into a search engine, to determine if the roadmap is still available.

1   Canadian aircraft companies technology roadmap
    http://www.ic.gc.ca/epic/site/ad-ad.nsf/en/ad03117e.html
2   American Aluminum Association's roadmap for aluminium
    http://www1.eere.energy.gov/industry/aluminum/pdfs/
    autoroadmap.pdf
3   American Aluminum Association's roadmap for the automotive sector
    http://www1.eere.energy.gov/industry/aluminum/pdfs/al_roadmap.pdf
4   US Department of Energy's Office of Advanced Automotive Technologies
    looking at end-of-life vehicles
    http://www.es.anl.gov/Energy_systems/CRADA_Team_Link/
    ELV%20Roadmap.pdf
5   American Plastics Council's roadmap for the 'plastic car'
    http://www.plastics-car.com/s_plasticscar/bin.asp?CID=547&DID=
    1816&DOC=FILE.PDF
6   http://monet.aber.ac.uk:8080/monet/docs/tg_minutes_and_reports/
    automotive/a1_report.pdf
7   Canadian shipbuilding industry roadmap
    http://www.nrc-cnrc.gc.ca/clusters/ocean/home_e.html
8   European Automotive Research Partners Association roadmap for future
    automotive research
    http://www.furore-network.com/documents/furore_rod_map_final.pdf
9   American Plastics Council roadmap on the future of plastics for automo-
    tives
    http://www.plasticscar.com/s_plasticscar/sec_inner.asp?TRACKID=&VID=
    105&CID=425&DID=1341
10 SRA from Advisory Council for Aeronautics Research in Europe
    http://www.acare4europe.com/docs/ASD-exec%20sum-2nd-final-171104-

out-asd.pdf
11 SRA from the European Road Transport Research Advisory Council
http://www.ertrac.org/pdf/publications/ertrac_agenda_dec2004.pdf
12 UK's Foresight Vehicle initiative
http://www.foresightvehicle.org.uk/public/info_/FV/TRMV2.pdf
13 http://lean.mit.edu/index.php?option=com_content&task=
view&id=355&Itemid=313
14 UK's National Composite Network roadmap for composites
http://www.ncn-uk.co.uk/DesktopDefault.aspx?tabindex=18&tabid=373
15 EU Nanoroad initiative on nanomaterials in the automotive sector
http://www.nanoroad.net/download/roadmap_ai.pdf
16 Euroforum SRA for Urban Mobility
http://www.eurforum.net/html/fileadmin/SRA_finalversion_
submitted.pdf
17 EU Technology Platform SRA for waterborne transport and operations
http://www.waterborne-tp.org/bal_ims_controler.php?menu=
MzRrMG5la2I4N2UwYzpnNg===&reset=search&page=1
18 European Association of Automotive Suppliers roadmap for the future of
automotive research
http://www.clepa.be/index.php?id=94
19 SRA from EU's High Altitude Aircraft and Airship Sensing Applications
group
http://www.pegasus4europe.com/pegasus/workshop/documents/
contributions/Barbier_full.pdf
20 Nanoforum.org report on Nanotechnology in Aerospace
http://www.nanoforum.org/nf06~modul~showmore~folder~99999~
scid~451~.html?action=longview_publication&

CHAPTER 6

ROADMAPS IN THE CONSTRUCTION INDUSTRY

CONTENTS

BACKGROUND

Both residential and commercial buildings are using increasingly complex and diverse technologies as the growth in population accelerates. These technologies are instigated by designers and architects for all aspects of a building's construction, operation, and maintenance.

The trends are to adopt 'intelligent' practices where the new technologies improve the quality of life and are as sustainable as possible. Security, comfort and accessibility, at low cost, are the goals, and several roadmaps have been drawn up by a number of countries to cover different aspects of the Construction Industry:

Window Industry Technology Roadmap
In April 2000, the US Department of Energy's Office of Building Technology, State and Community Program published a roadmap with a group of interested parties from the Window Industry (1). This was in response to changing market and business conditions, where new technology was expected to play a vital role in addressing the issues of energy conservation, enhanced quality, fast delivery, and low installation cost.

Windows offer added-value, and the participants took into account that:

- Windows are an integral part of a building
- Active, smart glass can provide energy, security, lighting, and aesthetics, and is an environmental solution
- There is an increased usage of glass and windows in buildings.

Suitable partnerships and funding were suggested, and priority technology actions were set down as seen in Table 6.1.

High-Performance Commercial Buildings – A Technology Roadmap
In 2000, the US Department of Energy's Office of Building

Table 6.1

Near-term (0-3 years)	• Define standards and protocols for integrating different building components • Develop strategies and hardware to optimise integrated building systems, with methods to measure their value • Define performance metrics for comfort, system integration, energy, cost, and environmental impacts • Establish a system for rating products on the basis of durability • Define appropriate durability and warranty periods for different window components
Mid-term (3-10 years	• Develop analytical tools to enable manufacturers to design and market efficient windows • Develop methods to measure and prove durability • Support, specify and identify applications for improved technology (including new materials and processes) • Develop products that encourage consumers to upgrade as features advance
Long-term (10-20 years)	• Develop long-term, integrated photovoltaic products • Develop superior insulating materials and components • Develop integrated electronics

Technology, State and Community Program, initiated a roadmap aimed at looking at the future of high-performance commercial buildings, addressing the complex and diverse technologies that go into their construction, operation and maintenance (2). Traditionally, building materials, components and subsystems have been designed and implemented with little regard for their inter-dependence. An example given in the report is that water heating loads are considered to be just a function of building, and are calculated independently of a building's plumbing design, where heat recovery from outgoing wastewater for pre-heating the incoming supply is not considered.

The proposals are that there should be a 'whole-buildings' approach, by combining research in the following fields: energy-efficient building shells; equipment; lighting; daylighting; windows; passive and active solar; photovoltaic; fuel cells; advanced sensors and controls; and combined heating, cooling and power.

Technology Roadmap for Intelligent Buildings

The Technology Roadmap for Intelligent Buildings (3) was a collaborative research project, carried out in 2002, between industry and five federal Canadian government departments and agencies, managed by the Continental Automated Buildings Association (CABA). The project focused on commercial, institutional and high-rise residential buildings, and culminated in a final report that provides an in-depth examination of intelligent buildings technologies. An example to illustrate the need for intelligent buildings technologies is the ability to access a building independently and securely outside of normal working hours.

Major benefits are listed:

- Standardised wiring enables swift upgrade of control systems
- Increased individual environmental control can lead to a higher value building and leasing potential
- Consumption costs are managed through zone control on a time of day basis
- Occupants control building systems after hours via computer or telephone
- Occupant use after hours is tracked for charge-back purposes
- Service or replacement history of individual relay and zone use can be tracked
- Only one resource is needed to modify telephone, security, parking, LAN, wireless devices, building directory, etc.

The 'actionable' recommendations and conclusions were:

- Intelligent building technologies are available but have not yet been widely adopted
- The development and construction industry is reluctant to accept intelligent technologies
- Many changes and initiatives must occur for the technologies to become widespread
- Promotion and education at all levels and in all segments of the industry is needed.

Building Construction Technology Roadmap

A Building Construction Roadmap was produced in 2004 for Australia to cope with the fact that, by 2025, three million more homes would need to be added to the eight million that already exist. The Copper Development Centre of Australia developed the roadmap with the University of Sydney with a focus on home building; it included, but was not limited to, applications for technologies involving copper (4). The roadmap outlined ten main characteristics for the house of the future:

- Flexibility, modularity and materials
- Water
- Energy
- Communication
- Security, safety and health
- User-friendliness, comfort and safety
- Home operations base
- Entertainment
- Smart services, appliances and fittings
- Maintenance management.

For each of the characteristics, the trends are listed, along with the issues related to the trends and consequential enabling technology requirements.

It is an excellent example of a technology roadmap and Table 6.2 is reproduced here for the first characteristic - *Flexibility, modularity and materials.*

Table 6.2

TRENDS	ISSUES	ENABLING TECHNOLOGIES
Prefab whole structure Prefab internal walls Relocatable modular internal walls	▪ Lack of skilled tradesmen ▪ High on-site costs ▪ Time consuming BCA approval process and regulations for joint, services and systems ▪ Need to de-skill site installations and increase speed of construction ▪ Internal layout needs to change simply as family and aging requirements change ▪ Internal walls designed for recycling	1. design assisted by artificial intelligence – virtual walkthrough using CAD for marketing 2. fast factory manufacture using CAD/CAM and CNC close tolerances 3. data collection forms basis of home instruction manual 4. wall and smart service loom connectors across joints 5. vertical and horizontal service ducts 6. develop flat wire cable looms to fit skirting/ducts, aiding future expansion 7. light weight non-load bearing partition type walls readily relocatable 8. levelling screws, floor and ceiling cover strips, acoustics approximately 40 dba
Prefab service modules, bathroom and kitchen	• Fast installation and inclusion of third pipe	9. factory manufactured complete unit or kit 10. complete with third pipe, smart wiring, etc 11. ditto kitchens including plumbing and smart wiring
Sensors embedded in walls Service looms embedded in ducts or skirtings	• Intelligent active environmental and security control systems • High resolution information • Convergence of media via digitalisation • Flexible access to power and communications	12. wireless micro systems for control of ventilation, temperature, lighting and energy usage, water quality (10-15 years from market as of 2004) 13. flat wire looms and multi-capacity ducts / skirtings
Smart windows	▪ Thermal, optical and acoustic control	14. integrated photovoltaics 15. films incorporating nanoparticles (e.g. ZnO, Au) for spectral selectivity giving reflectivity and thermal control 16. holographic/imaging projection 17. organic light emitting diode (OLED) embedded in conducting polymer layer in laminated windows 18. switchable between transparent and opaque (e.g. SPD smart glass) 19. integrally able to communicate to central control
Surface coatings	• Self cleaning • Stain and mould resistance • Corrosion inhibition • Friction modification • Optical control of surfaces	20. nano coatings, e.g. TiO2 (photocatalytic, hydrophilic), Si-based (lotus effect, superhydrophobic), oliophobic
Ducted sunlight	• Reduce energy consumption and improve ambience	21. polymer fibre optics for piping light 22. skylights using smart windows technology adapted to polymers 23. LEDs as alternative to incandescent and fluorescent light sources
Textured finishes away from natural brick	• Widens aesthetic possibilities • Lack of bricklaying skills	24. pressed, roll formed surfaces/products cementitious and new coating
Insulation	• Energy reduction • Improved temperature control	25. smart windows, improved thermal properties, R values of shell of structure 26. new insulation materials e.g. aerogels
Recyclable materials	• Reduced waste	27. develop materials that can be split into components for easy recycling

FLEXIBILITY, MODULARITY & MATERIALS

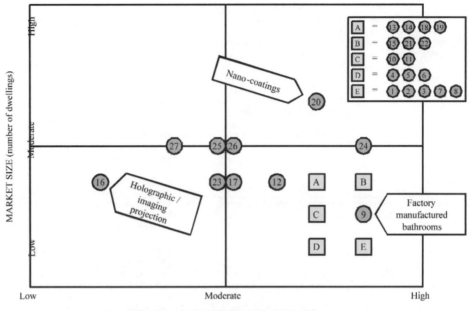

Figure 6.1

The 27 'enabling technologies' were then displayed on a matrix (Figure 6.1) which takes into account the likely market size in 2025, and the current (2005) availability of the enabling technology.

Three items have been noted here to show the impact and expectations for nanocoatings; bathrooms manufactured outside the home; and the lower potential for holographic / imaging projection.

Matrices are produced for the other characteristics. It is interesting to note that the roadmap is the first to highlight the opportunities that are likely to be brought about by nanotechnology, which is discussed later in this chapter.

Other features are that prefabrication and off-site construction will increase, and there will be more flexibility in design to take account of lifestyle changes. Maintenance and servicing will be very different with self-cleaning surfaces inside and out, monitoring things such as structural defects, use of longer-life coatings, and use of online diagnostics for appliances.

The Australian roadmap goes into detail about the changes in how construction and design will cope with changes in the use of water, energy and communications. It is unlikely to be just an Australian problem but the suggestion is for a third water pipe in houses that will be used for the collection and re-use of 'grey' water driven by sanctions and rewards. Here the suggestion is that multi-functional nano-porous filtration for removal of chemical and biological impurities in water will be used.

Increased pressure to conserve energy will see the increasing use of smart metering, and embedded technology to run smart appliances and automated management. This will require micro and nano sensor development.

For communications, the home will have increased data and connectivity capacity with smart wiring, wireless, and self-diagnosis of problems. Again nano-sensors will play a major role.

This is a model roadmap, and unlike many others it does not just cover general aspects, it goes into considerable detail.

Strategic Research Agenda for the European Construction Sector
One of the European Union's Technology Platforms is ECTP (European Construction Technology Platform) and in December 2005 it published a Strategic Research Agenda (SRA) to provide a vision for the construction sector in Europe up to 2030 (5).

The document sets out to preserve Europe's heritage, and balance that with the demand for high quality standards for the future. Anticipated social needs demand that the construction sector can provide the following:

- Creating a built environment that is accessible and usable for all
- Providing well-designed, energy-efficient housing for all
- Improving health, safety and security of the built environment

- Contributing to objectives of the Kyoto Protocol (reduction of greenhouse gas emissions and more efficient use of energy)
- Adapting to climate change
- Preserving the natural environment and natural resources
- Preserving Europe's cultural heritage
- Enhancing the urban environment
- Maintaining a high level of efficiency and service the patrimony of infrastructure systems
- Optimising the life-cycle cost of the built environment
- Improving health and safety conditions in the construction sector.

This opens up many challenges, which are addressed by the Strategic Research Agenda. The priorities are detailed under the following headings:

Meeting user requirements
- Healthy, safe, and accessible indoor environment for all
- A new image of cities
- Efficient use of underground city space
- Mobility and supply through efficient networks

Becoming sustainable
- Reduce resource consumption (energy, water, materials)
- Reduce environmental and man-made impacts
- Sustainable management of transport and utilities networks
- A living cultural heritage for an attractive Europe
- Improve safety and security

Transformation of the construction sector
- A new client-driven, knowledge-based construction process
- ICT and automation
- High added-value construction materials
- Attractive workplace

Research Priorities for the UK Built Environment

In 2006, the UK National Platform for the Built Environment took the European SRA as a starting point for defining the UK's research priorities (6), and published a leaflet highlighting the priorities. In the UK, the built environment industry represents 20% of the UK's GDP.

The priorities set by the experts were under three headings

Reduced resource consumption
*   Efficient and renewable energy concepts, technologies and tools for new and existing buildings
*   Zero energy consuming and CO_2 emitting buildings
*   Environmentally friendly manufacturing technologies for construction materials and components
*   Training, dissemination and legislation to support reduced energy consumption

New client-driven, knowledge-based construction process
*   Tools, knowledge-bases and metrics to better understand both customer requirements and construction processes and products
*   Better products and processes based on knowledge of their application and ability to deliver to both industry and its customers
*   Databases and tools for whole life cost and value assessments

ICT and automation:
*   Development of industry standards and effective de-facto standards for data exchange, object definitions, and integrated model servers
*   ICT tools for the efficient connection of all those involved in mobile sites to corporate information networks, incorporating readily available health and safety knowledge throughout
*   Development of new visualisation, virtual reality and communication tools, based on advanced ICT systems and using shared integrated data models to enable a value

assessment of the built environment
- The development of new off-site manufacturing systems, automation and mechanisation.

Technology Roadmap for Composites in the Construction Industry
The UK's National Composite Network (NCN), which is part of the UK Materials Knowledge Transfer Network (KTN), has produced a number of roadmaps on composites for different industry sectors. The one for the construction industry, issued in June 2006, may be found by registering at their web page (7). Composites are seeing considerable growth in a variety of areas, and although 'plastics' and 'composites' imply 'cheap and nasty' growth is likely to escalate. Certainly, better promotion of composites for the construction industry is required. The recommendations from the roadmapping exercise were:

- More attention directed to standards for quality assurance and design, with codes of practice
- More effort on understanding joints and connections, with attention to durability of joints and characterisation of joint behaviour.
- Focus is needed on composites working in harmony with other materials
- Generally, more R&D is needed on durability, life cycle analysis, whole life cost, and any environmental issues.

Nanoforum Report – Nanotechnology and Construction
Although not strictly a roadmap, Nanoforum.org, which is the EU's Nanotechnology Gateway, produced a report in November 2006 on Nanotechnology and Construction. It may be obtained free of charge by registering through the web site (8)

The report contains an introduction to nanotechnology and goes on to discuss its impact on current uses in the construction sector. Concrete and steel are now tougher thanks to 'nano-structuring', and other applications quoted include self-cleaning glass. Increasing strength and durability helps the environment by the efficient use of resources. Two nano-sized particles are highlighted because they are likely to have a large affect on buildings. Titanium dioxide is being used to breakdown dirt, not just as a coating on self-clean glass, but as a coating on buildings to catalyse the breakdown of pollution. Carbon nanotubes (CNT), have phenomenal strength, and are beginning to be used in materials in the sector.

A comment from the report is worth quoting:

"If construction continues to ignore nanotechnology, it will be the one left paying a fortune for a last minute ticket it could have had for a song if it had acted earlier".

Although the Nanoforum report does not go into much detail, there are examples in the leisure and automotive sectors that are already employing nanotechnology to provide improved products. Wilson Sports have nanocomposite tennis racquets that have enabled Federer to hit the ball even harder, and with more accuracy. The Wilson Double Core tennis ball has a nanocomposite butyl rubber layer on the inside that keeps the air in the ball.

Just as automotive development products are perfected in Formula 1 cars before they arrive in our own cars, some of the developments described above will find applications in building construction; certainly the barrier property applications could be an early opportunity.

Nano-coatings are already on the market to provide hydrophobicity for fabric, wood and masonry applications, and in the bathroom it is possible to get glass for showers that do not have water droplets left on them. Anti-scratch surfaces are being used as the final lacquer on Mercedes cars, and this is being examined for other surfaces. Other nano-coatings give superior anti-corrosion properties over conventional products. Samsung are using silver nanoparticles to provide anti-microbial surfaces for washing machines and refrigerators. Other companies are known to be developing anti-microbial nano-surfaces for kitchen and bathroom surfaces for stain and mould resistance. There are even nano-coatings being promoted that are 'anti-fingerprint', which keep chrome or glass looking fresh and clean. The list of functional coatings is extensive, and as the costs reduce, the markets will rise rapidly.

Other nanotechnology opportunities that are at an early stage are improved sealants, adhesives and flame-retardant materials. The conclusion from the Nanoforum report is that the sheer size and scope of nanotechnology for the construction industry means that the accompanying economic impact will be huge.

NanoByg – a Survey of Nanoinnovation in Danish Construction

Realising the future impact of nanotechnology, the Danish construction sector have produced (May 2007) a survey of nano-innovation in Danish construction (9). The partners compared the development of nanotechnology with the need for renewal in construction and came up with six nano-thematic pillars:

- Nanostructured materials
- Nanostructured surfaces
- Nano-optics
- Nano-sensors and electronics
- Nano-related integrated energy production and storage
- Nano-related integrated environmental remediation.

With a co-ordinated effort, the Danes foresee that they will make a major impact with nanotechnology applications for the construction sector. The report goes into quite a lot of detail but provides the following summary table which lists the relevance of the themes to the construction sector:

Others

In September 2000, Forintek Canada Corp produced a Lumber and Added-Value Wood Products Technology Roadmap (10) but it is concerned with trends in processing wood. Although there is a section on 'breakthrough technologies', these too cover new processes for wood products.

146

Table 6.3

Nano-thematic Pillar	Application in	Important properties

1. Nano-structured materials
 	
  1. composites
  2. wood
  3. nanoporous materials
  4. polymers
  5. other materials
	Insulation materials
	Load carrying materials
	Interior construction materials
	Exterior construction materials
	Surfaces
		Strength, lightness, durability
		Production and execution
		Indoor climate
		Maintenance
		Energy efficiency
		Resource efficiency
		Recyclability
		Degradability
		Fire protection

2. Functional surfaces
 	
  1. chemically modified surfaces
  2. physically modified surfaces
	Building surfaces
	Water systems
	Coating of load carrying materials
	Ventilation, heating, electrical, lighting, sensors, integrated functions
		Durability
		Cleaning
		Hygiene
		Maintenance
		Strength

3. Optics
 	
  1. planar lightwave circuits
  2. photonic crystal fibres
  3. light emitting diodes (LED)
  4. integrated optical sensors
	Sensors, integrated functions
	Electrical and lighting systems
	Fibre cables
		Energy efficiency
		Climate control
		Fire and other safety
		Cleaning

4. Sensors and electonics
 	
  1. monitoring
  2. transmission
	Bio-, optical, chemical, micromechanical, microorganism sensors
	Electroactive materials
	Water systems
		Monitoring and control
		Integrated functions in electrical and lighting systems

5. Integrated energy production and distribution / storage
  1. fuel cells
  2. solar cells
  3. other
	Solar cells
	Hydrogen storage
	Fuel cells
	Exterior materials
	Ventilation and heating
		Energy efficiency and self-sufficiency
		Resource efficiency
		Indoor climate

6. Integrated environmental control
  1. catalytic cleaning
  2. other separation / cleaning processes
  3. characterisation
	Water systems (supply and waste)
	Catalysis
	Separation processes
	Waste systems
		Cleaning and hygiene
		Indoor climate
		Integrated functions
		Degradability
		Resource efficiency
		Energy efficiency
		Substitution of hazardous materials
		Production and execution

General nano-research and competencies
  1. Synthesis
  2. Manufacturing
  3. Characterisation
	Fundamental material understanding and design	

A Wood-based Panel Products Technology Roadmap (11) was published in 2005 and then updated in June 2006. It was produced through Industry Canada and Forintek, but again emphasis is on manufacturing routes for wood panels. Goals and technology priorities fall into one of five categories: fibre supply, manufacturing costs, product attributes and performance, new products, and environmental issues.

The wood composite panel industry is, of course, looking at new products, either to diversify their production when commodities suffer from competition and consequential low prices, or to add value to existing products by accessing niche markets. Trends are to avoid the use of formaldehyde; reduce weight; modify surfaces to enhance surface characteristics and machinability; use improved adhesives; treatment of wood to make it more resistant to UV degradation and weathering; improve fire performance; and be as environmentally friendly as possible.

Work is in hand to produce hybrid products, where wood is combined with cement, plastics, metals and glass or carbon fibres to achieve superior mechanical performance.

REFERENCES

Some of the roadmaps referenced here may be obtained in hard copy from the organisations producing them, but the easiest way to access them is through the web references, which are given below. Should hard copies be required, then they can be printed off, or these same references may help with providing the right contacts to approach for paper copies. However, as time progresses, web sites go through changes, so some of the references may fall out of date. In these cases, it is suggested that the title of the roadmap is fed into a search engine, to determine if the roadmap is still available.

1   US Department of Energy's Office of Building Technology, State and Community Program roadmap for the US window industry
    http://www.eere.energy.gov/buildings/info/documents/pdfs/27994.pdf
2   US Department of roadmap for commercial buildings
    http://www.eere.energy.gov/buildings/info/documents/pdfs/roadmap_lowres.pdf
3   Canadian industry roadmap for intelligent buildings

http://www.caba.org/trm/TRM_English.pdf

4   Australian Building Construction Technology Roadmap
http://www.copper.com.au/cdc/technology_roadmap/roadmap/index.html.

5   SRA from the European Construction Technology Platform
http://www.ectp.org/documentation/ECTP-SRA-2005_12_23.pdf

6   Roadmap for the UK National Platform for the Built Environment
http://www.nationalplatform.org.uk/downloads/UKSRA FinalBrochure.pdf.

7   UK's National Composites Network for composites in the construction industry
http://www.ncn-uk.co.uk/DesktopModules/ViewDocument.aspx?DocumentID=564.

8   Nanoforum.org report on Nanotechnology and Construction
http://www.nanoforum.org/nf06~modul~showmore~folder~99999

9   Nano-innovation in the Danish construction sector
http://www.nanet.nu/upload/centre/nanet/nanobyg /nanobyg_a%20survey%20of%20nanoinnovation%20in%20danish%20construction.pdf

10   Industry Canada roadmap on Lumber and Added-value Wood Products
http://www.ic.gc.ca/epic/site/fi-if.nsf/en/fb01315e.html

11   Industry Canada roadmap covering wood-based panel products
http://www.ic.gc.ca/epic/site/fi-if.nsf/en/oc01500e.html

CHAPTER 7

ROADMAPS IN THE ELECTRONICS INDUSTRY

CONTENTS

BACKGROUND

The electronics industry, and in particular the semiconductor industry, was the driving force for the development of many technology-based products in the twentieth century and, combined with materials, will be their driver in the twenty-first century. These products were, and continue to be, the basis for advancement and market success of many other industry sectors, notably telecommunications and computers.

Electronics started in 1904 with the invention of the electron tube by John Fleming (1). Soon after, in 1906, it was developed into the three-element tube that led to the production of commercial radios in the 1920s. This laid the foundation to a communication and enter- tainments industry. These made a significant leap forward in 1947 by the invention of the transistor by William Shockley and his associates at Bell Laboratories in the USA (2). It was a semiconductor, based on the physical and chemical properties of silicon and its oxides. The development of the process technology for low cost, mass produc- tion, made the semiconductor industry one of most successful of the century. It initiated component and system miniaturisation.

Integrated circuits were developed in the 1950s, allowing the integration of many circuits with hundreds of components into one circuit. The introduction of analogue devices in the 1960s vastly increased the amount of information that could be stored on a single silicon chip. This inaugurated a revolution in the computer industry. It led to the introduction of the personal computer and the beginning of multi-billion dollar global businesses in communications, comput- ers and consumer goods such as cellular telephones, television sets, medical equipment etc.

In the 1980s, American manufacturers became the world leaders in semiconductor development and assembly. While U.S. companies are still a major presence in the semiconductor industry (representing about 40% of world sales in 1998), the consumer items that result from the use of components are mostly manufactured in Asia. The European Union's expansion in 2004 created an electronics market that covered 25 countries and was estimated to have a value of more than \$285 billion in 2005. It too has continued to grow but is striving to be competitive with Asia. Worldwide electronic sales exceeded \$700 billion in 1997. At the end of 2005, the total global market for electronics, including opto and micro, was over \$1 trillion. The microchip industry drives the information technology sector which makes a significant contribution to the GDP of many nations.

Now, in the twenty-first century, advances in materials technology and ink-jet printing have combined with microelectronics, to grow an industry in printable electronics. Printable electronics is the use of low-cost, high-speed printing technologies to create electronic circuits and devices. It will change the economics of the electronics industry and create new kinds of products. Circuitry is made using nanometallic and polymer inks, laid down using either conventional printing technologies, such as offset, or using ink-jet printing. This field is commonly known as polymer or organic electronics.

Polymer electronic devices utilise the semiconductor properties of polymer materials that are similar to conventional silicon. They can be produced using simpler manufacturing processes. Thin film transistors made with polymer electronics will be used in a wide range of electronics applications, including electronic paper, flat panel displays, electronic tags and labels, smart cards, embedded solar cells, wall coverings, memory, and wearable computing. Hence the technology has the potential to radically change the economics of key segments of industry. This convergence of materials and printing technology is likely to revolutionise electronic products in the same way as the invention of the silicon transistor did in the 1940s. These will impact working practices and transform business, particularly in the retail and commerce sectors.

The impressive growth rate of microelectronics in the 1990s has generated a multi-billion dollar industry but the reduction in scale to accommodate more functionality and higher storage capacity on a microchip is now placing limits on the capability of (CMOS) Complementary Metal Oxide Semiconductor technology. CMOS is a major class of integrated circuits used in microprocessors. It has been forecasted that by 2014 the minimum feature size for memories and microprocessors will be approaching 35nm. Beyond this, new fabrication processes based on nanotechnology will be required. Alternative solutions that operate in the nanoscale regime that permit a smooth transition from CMOS technology are the subject of intense research by major companies.

The above technological developments will give increase impetus to the markets for new products. The global sales of electronic products, particularly in communications and computers are significant drivers of the world-wide economy. The revenue derived from the consumer electronics industry is expected to reach $700 Billion by 2009. The fastest growth in both volume and revenue from consumer demand will be in mobile phone products, television and computers will be the main contributors to the expected growth. China and other Asian countries with expanding populations and economies will dominate the consumer market. Continuous innovation and the development of new materials are likely to add to the existing sales predictions for electronic-based products.

An example of a new area of development based on nanomaterials is an understanding of the unique properties of carbon nanotubes (CNTs) (3) (4) and their potential impact on their use in nanoelectronics. CNTs are already used in the construction of sports products such as golf clubs, tennis rackets, and baseball bats. Currently applications in electronics account for about 10% of the global market for CNTs with a value of about $80 million. As more industries and companies see the advantages of this material then the market can be expected to grow significantly in the future.

The very competitive electronics industry, led by microelectronics and the emergent nanomaterials technologies are producing new smaller, lighter, faster, more functional electronics products more quickly and economically than ever before. There has never been a greater need to plan ahead for the electronics–based industries.

Industrialists and planners therefore need to have advanced knowledge on scientific and technological developments related to microelectronics, its associated fields and its spin-off industries to retain competitiveness for their companies. Roadmapping is now recognised as the basic tool for doing this so all major organisations representing the industries regularly review and update their roadmaps.

There are a plethora of national and international roadmaps covering all aspects of electronics, including components, systems and products. This is not surprising owing to the huge growth in demand for new electronic-based products. The global markets will continue to grow at an increasing rate and may exceed all current estimates.

ROADMAPS

The Semiconductor Industry Association (SIA) is the premier trade association representing the U.S. semiconductor industry. Founded in 1977 by five microelectronics innovators, SIA unites 95 companies responsible for more than 85 percent of semiconductor production in US (5). It produced an American style roadmap, the National Technology Roadmap for Semiconductors (NTRS) (6). In 1998, the SIA became closer to its European, Japanese, Korean and Taiwanese counterparts by creating the first global roadmap: The International Technology Roadmap for Semiconductors (ITRS). This international group has over 1000 companies which were affiliated with working groups within the ITRS.

The five international sponsors and contributors to the roadmaps are as follows:

1. European Semiconductor Industry Association
2. Japan Electronics and Information Technology Industries Association
3. Korean Semiconductor Industry Association
4. Semiconductor Industry Association
5. Taiwan Semiconductor Industry Association

International Technology Roadmaps for Semiconductors (ITRS) (7)
The first international roadmap was published in 1999 as a joint effort by European, and Asian contributors. Since then it has been updated

in even-numbered years and fully revised in odd numbered years to 2007. The objective of this roadmap is to present industry-wide consensus on the industry's research and development needs for a 15 year horizon. This objective has been accomplished by providing a forum for international discussion, co-operation, and agreement among the leading semiconductor manufacturers and the leading suppliers of equipment, materials and software. It also includes researchers from university, consortia, and government labs. It is the most comprehensive document that exists for helping investment decisions at all levels in the industry.

The basic premise of this roadmap and others is that continued scaling of components and systems would further reduce costs per function and thus promote market growth to stay within Moore's Law (8). The exponential decrease in minimum feature size used to fabricate integrated circuits coupled to the decreasing cost-per-function have been the most significant drivers for the wider availability of computers, industrial and consumer products. An example of economic and social significance was the miniaturisation of a switch that enabled telephones to be linked by radio thus allowing mobile phones to be used. The low production costs evolved into a global multi-billion dollar industry. The improvement trends for ICs enabled by feature scaling are shown in Table 7.1

To indicate the current evolution of the ITRS roadmaps we summarise the latest two editions below. They can also be seen on the internet website (9).

The 2005 Edition of ITRS

The 2005 ITRS represented a major departure from the previous versions of Roadmaps because it removed the concept of technology node as the main pace setter for the IC market. In computers, the volume of data that can be stored is of paramount importance. The key element is the *dynamic random access memory* (DRAM) which stores each bit of data in a separate capacitor within an integrated circuit. The development of DRAM products set the technology pace. As device features become smaller, other technologies were produc-

Table 7.1

TREND	EXAMPLE
Integration Level	Components/Chip, Moore's Law
Cost	Cost per function
Speed	Microprocessor throughput
Power	Laptop or cell phone battery life
Compactness	Small and light-weight products
Functionality	Non-volatile memory, imager

ing even smaller and faster than the DRAM. As a result, the use of a single number such as a technology node, derived from the half-pitch of DRAM, no longer characterised the whole semiconductor industry.

The 2005 ITRS roadmap also indicated the growing interest in new nanoscale devices representing alternatives to *complementary metal oxide semiconductors* (CMOS). In the roadmap, topics such as Emerging Research Devices and Integration, Devices and Structures were addressed in a separate chapter from the 'Process' Chapter. It stated *'that although CMOS is, and will remain, the industry workhorse up to and beyond the year 2020, new devices will be introduced in the latter half of the next decade utilising different and new ways of processing and storing information.'* Most of the proposed devices rely very heavily on new material properties and therefore, a new sub-chapter on 'Emerging Research Materials' was added to the roadmap.

The 2007 ITRS Edition
In the 2007 edition of the ITRS, international technology working groups produced technology-area chapters. They focused on the following: system drivers, test and test equipment, process integration, devices and structures, radiofrequency and analogue wireless communications, emerging research devices, front-end processes, lithography, interconnect, factory integration, assembly and packaging, metrology, environment safety and health and modelling and simulation.

International Electronics Manufacturing Initiative (INEMI) (10)

The INEMI is an industry-led consortium of approximately 70 electronics manufacturers, suppliers and related organizations. Their mission is to identify and close technology gaps, which includes the development and integration of the electronics industry supply infrastructure. It has initiated a global roadmap study for 2009 with the first meeting held in 2008 hosted by Hewlett-Packard (HP).

The International Microelectronics and Packaging Society (IMAPS) (11)

IMAPS is the largest society dedicated to the advancement and growth of microelectronics and electronics packaging technologies through professional education. Founded in 1967, it is the leading international microelectronics and electronic packaging society with professional members in 23 North American chapters and 21 international chapters. Members of the Society represent every discipline and speciality in the electronics industry and include both technical and marketing professionals.

IMAPS has begun a study of the two most widely used industry roadmaps, the International Technology Roadmap for Semi-conductors (ITRS) and the roadmap of the International Electronics Manufacturing Initiative (iNEMI). Where ITRS is centred on technical chip-level challenges, the iNEMI roadmap addresses upcoming requirements at higher levels of integration.

Report on Asian Semiconductor Manufacturing (12) (13)

This report is part of In-Stat's Asia Semiconductor & Manufacturing Service, which tracks semiconductor consumption by application and by country. This service forecasts application segments in crucial Asian markets, including China, India, Japan, Korea and Taiwan. Semiconductor manufacturing is also addressed by country. It includes a forecast of Asian foundry revenue, its market share of the foundry business, as well as of the overall semiconductor market up to 2010. It also includes extensive analysis of the challenges and drivers of the Asian semiconductor industry. The report also includes some technology roadmaps from major manufacturers. With the semiconductor supply chain already strongly established in Asia, including design and testing and packaging services, the long-term outlook indicates that Asia's position in semiconductor production will continue to strengthen. China is expected to drive the next manufacturing growth wave in Asia.

Roadmaps for Printable Electronics
Printable electronics may be defined as the use of printing technologies to create electronic circuits and devices. Both conductive organic polymer inks and nanometallic inks are used in the printing processes. Printable electronics is gaining increased attention owing to its economic benefits and business opportunities it presents for a whole range of novel products. It has the potential to radically change the economics of key segments of the semiconductor industry. The most recent product roadmap for printable electronics predicts the applications and products that will reach the market by 2010 based on the assumption that technology will develop and demand will rise (14). The products listed in the roadmap are shown in Table 7.2.

The roadmap provides a critical analysis of the markets for printable electronics. It is intended to be a guide for business strategists, marketing and business development executives, product managers and technologists within electronics companies, specialty chemical and materials firms, printing and printing equipment companies, and electronic manufacturing equipment firms. It is also designed for investment banks, venture capitalists and internal investment teams that are looking at investments in printable electronics.

The authors of the roadmap question the maturity of the technology to capture markets for RFID tags, solar panels, portable book readers etc. Printable electronics is likely to lead a new generation of products.

Already a number of companies are producing products and others have been granted licences to manufacture by those who have pioneered research and development. Cambridge Display Technology (CDT), originally a university spin-out company, is now

Table 7.2

DISPLAYS
Computer Displays
Printed backplanes for LCD screens
Printed OLED based computer screens
Mobile communications displays
Printed main displays
Flexible displays
Television displays
Small novelty-like television displays
Advertising displays
Smart-shelving
Electronic magazine advertising
Sizeable high resolution FPDs
Other consumer displays
Small displays for consumer

RFIDs
Printable antennas
Low to moderate volume tags for palette-level RFIDs
High volume, RFID tagging as barcode replacement
PHOTOVOLTAICS Small arrays for portable
Electronics Products for use in buildings
LIGHTING Some novelty lighting
Specialty lighting applications
SENSORS Sensor arrays Wearable
Computing applications
KEYBOARDS
Membrane
keyboards

TOYS AND
NOVELTIES
Greeting cards
Toys
SMART CARDS
AND TICKETING
Smart tickets and passes
Smart cards
CHIPS:
Plastic logic and processors
Non-embedded products
Non-embedded memories

a subsidiary of Sumitomo Chemical of Japan and leads the development of display technology based on polymer organic light emitting diodes. These offer superior performance characteristics to other display technologies, such as liquid crystal displays, in many applications. The company's light emitting polymer (LEP) technology is targeted for use in a wide range of electronic display products used for information management, communications and entertainment.

Another spin-out company, Plastic Logic from Cambridge University, recently opened its manufacturing plant in Germany. The company has a growing portfolio of patents based on ink-jet printing of active electronic circuits using advanced plastic materials. This technology has the potential to radically change the economics of key segments of the semiconductor industry. Flexible substrates are now a practical possibility. Capital costs will be significantly lower than for silicon by eliminating conventional photolithography, vacuum processing and high temperatures. Initial market opportunities include active matrix backplanes for displays and electronic labels - the natural successor to bar codes and magnetic stripe cards.

The projections given by the roadmap for printable electronics up to 2010 are shown in Table 7.3.

Early products for printable electronics include RFID tags, smart shelving and packaging.

Technology Roadmap for Nanoelectronics (15)
The 2nd edition of the Technology Roadmap for Nanoelectronics published in November 2000 follows the same format as an earlier edition published in April 1999. It was carried out with support from the European Commission's IST programme for 'Future and Emerging Technologies'. The Roadmap's six chapters and an annex include: A Review of Markets and Applications, Emerging Devices, Nanofabrication and Circuits and Systems.

The Roadmap examines the technology, market and economic issues associated with extending CMOS technology and moving into new processes to achieve smaller feature sizes and higher densities on chips. Next generation lithography options, based on (EUV), X-ray,

Table 7.3

	2006	2007	2008	2009	2010
DISPLAYS					
Computer Displays		Printed back-planes for LCD screens	Printed OLED-based computer screens	Flexible Displays	
Mobile phone displays	Printed sub-displays			Flexible Displays	
Television displays			Small novelty-like TV displays		
Advertisng displays		Smart shelving	Electronic magazine advertising		
Other product displays	Small displays for consumer electronic devices		Displays for smart packaging		
RFIDs		Printable antennas	Volume palette-level RFIDs		High volume RDIF tags as bar-code replacement
PHOTOVOLTAICS		Small arrays for portable electronics		Products for use in buildings	
LIGHTING			Some novelty lighting		Speciality lighting applications
SENSORS		Sensor arrays	Wearable computer applications		
MEMBRANE KEYBOARDS		Membrane keyboard			
TOYS AND NOVELTIES	Greetings cards	toys			
SMART CARDS AND TICKETING		Smart tickets and passes	Smart cards		
CHIPS					
Plastic logic					Non-embebbed products
Memory			Non-embedded products		

projection electron-beam and projection ion-beam lithographies were being evaluated. It is believed that optical lithography could be used for the 100nm technology node. Minimum feature sizes for CMOS technology is now moving towards 35nm which is expected to be established in 2014.

Molecular Nanoelectronics can provide switching at the single molecule level compared to bulk based molecular electronics, which have found numerous applications as liquid crystals in displays, dye lasers, light emitting diodes or plastic transistors. Hybrid molecular electronics holds the possibility of cost-effective production of self-assembly circuits, using chemical or biological reactions that will match the ultimate densities obtainable with CMOS technologies (16).

The ultimate aim is to make molecular logic and memory elements in circuits. With bit densities of 1012 bits/cm^2, to reduce switching cycle times to a few picoseconds and to limit the energy per bit cycle to 10 MeV. This has yet to be achieved but the roadmap indicates that molecular nanoelectronics has the potential to produce sub-nanometre sized functional devices using bottom-up nanotechnology processes.

Roadmap for Nanoelectronics Policy (17)
The Roadmap is incorporated in the report 'Vision 2020: Nanoelectronics' produced by some leading European companies to present to the European Commission. It outlined a strategy for nanoelectronics that included investment from private and public sources to be at least €6 billion by 2008 and the setting up of a European Nanoelectronics Initiative Advisory Council (ENIAC) as a Technology Platform for Nanoelectronics (18)

The principal mission of ENIAC is to be 'The European Technology Platform on Nanoelectronics'. Its mission is to bring together leading players to develop and implement a coherent European vision for Nanoelectronics. This will be implemented by pursuing the following:

• Provide a strategic research agenda for the nanoelectronics sector, with respect to R&D
• Set out strategies and roadmaps to achieve this vision through the Strategic Research Agenda and other associated documents
• Stimulate increased and more effective and coherent public

and private investment in R&D in the nanoelectronics sector

- Contribute to improving convergence between EC, national, regional and private R&D actions on nanoelectronics within the European Research Area Framework
- Enhance networking and clustering of the R&D capacity in Europe
- Promote European commitment to R&D thus ensuring Europe as an attractive location for researchers
- Interact with other policies and actors at all levels that influence the competitiveness of the sector such as education and training, competition, IPR, finance and investment, etc.

This initiative is a prime example of where an Emergent Technology Roadmap can set out a strategic agenda for the future.

Roadmap for Nanoelectronics Standards (NESR), (19)
The Institute of Electrical and Electronics Engineers (IEEE) completed its Nanoelectronics Standards Roadmap (NESR), which establishes a framework for creating standards to help industry transition electronic applications based on nanotechnology from the laboratory to commercial use.

In 2007, the roadmap recommended the initiation of five nano-electronic standards: three for nanomaterials involving conductive interconnects, organic sensor structures and nano-dispersions and two for nano-devices involving nanoscale sensors and nanoscale emitting devices.

This roadmap is an essential document for manufacturing industry at a time when new processes are being established and Government regularity bodies are reviewing the health and safety aspects of new practices. The semiconductor industry was highly successful because it had set up strict manufacturing standards. Now that we are entering nanoscale production processes involving new materials, unique opportunities exist to maximise the benefits of this new technology.

A European Roadmap for Photonics and Nanotechnologies (20)

The MONA (Merging Optics and Nanotechnologies) consortium has developed this roadmap for photonics and nanotechnologies in Europe. This comprehensive roadmap has nine chapters and five annexes and was the result of two years' work with contributions from over 300 experts from industry and academia. It covers the future of materials, equipment, processes and applications and provides an outlook for the future development of nanophotonics.

The MONA roadmap identifies the following key nanomaterials that will have the most impact in photonics.

- Quantum dots and wires
- Plasmonic nanostructures
- Carbon nanotubes
- Integration of electronics with photonics
- Nanoparticles in glasses or polymers

A recent review given by Pavesi (21) shows there are many new potential nanophotonics applications, particularly now that photonics structures are beginning to be implemented in silicon. These include: communications, computing, information displays, optical and- infrared imaging, medicine, optical printing, optical command-and-control, optical sensing of physical and chemical and biological inputs, optical signal processing, optical storage and control of microwave devices and systems.

REFERENCES

Some of the roadmaps referenced here may be obtained in hard copy from the organisations producing them, but the easiest way to access them is through the web references, which are given below. Should hard copies be required, then they can be printed off, or these same references may help with providing the right contacts to approach for paper copies. However, as time progresses, web sites go through changes, so some of the references may fall out of date. In these cases, it is suggested that the title of the roadmap is fed into a search engine, to determine if the roadmap is still available.

1   Fleming, J.A.., 'The Thermionic Valve and Developments in Radio Telegraphy and Telephony', The Wireless Press, LTD, 1919.
2   Shockley, W., Bell Laboratories on December 16, 1947, http://www.cedmagic.com/history/transistor-1947.html
3   Charlier, C., et al., Electronic and Transport Properties of Nanotubes, Review of Modern Physics, 79, 677, 2007.
4   Collins, P., et al., 'Engineering Carbon Nanotubes and Nanotube Circuits', April 27, 2001.
5   Semiconductor Industry Association (SIA), http://www.sia-online.org/about
6   National Technology Roadmap for Semiconductors, Semiconductor Industry Association, San Jose, CA, 1994, 1997
7   International Roadmap for Semiconductors, August 2007, http:// www.itrs.net
8   Moore, G., 'Cramming More Components into Integrated Circuits', Electronics Magazine 19 April 1965: (Moore's Law)*.
9   ITRS 2005- International Technology Roadmap for Semiconductors, http://en.wikipedia.org/wiki/ and (htpp://www.itrs.net)
10   International Electronics Manufacturing Initiative (INEMI), http://inemi.org/cms/roadmapping/2007_iMEMI_Roadmap.html
11   The International Microelectronics and Packaging Society (IMAPS), http://www.impas.org.uk
12   http://www.nanomarkets.net/products/
13   http://www.the-infoshop.com/study/if11084_microelectronics_asia
14   Gasman, L., Roadmap for Printable Electronics, August 2005, http://www.nanoinfo.jp/whitepaper/nano-08-05pdf
15   Roadmap in Nanoelectronics, http://www.cordis.europa.eu/ nanotechnology/src/pub-nanoelectronics.htm
16   Joachim, C., et al 'From Molecular to Monomolecular Electronics', Nature, 408, 541-548, 30 November 2000.
17   'Materials Today', Volume 7, Issue 9, Page 18, September 2004.
18   http://eniac.eu/web.about/local_index.php
19   http://standards.ieee.org/announcements/nano/07/Nano07.html.
20   MONO-A European Roadmap for Photonics and Nanotechnology http://www.ist-mona.org/pdf?MONA_v13.pdf
21   Pavesi, I., 'Will Silicon Be the Photonic Material of the 3rd Millennium?', J. Phys. Condensed Matter 15, R1169 – R1196, 2004 (U. di Trento).

CHAPTER 8

ROADMAPS IN ENERGY SUPPLY

CONTENTS

BACKGROUND

There are a number of roadmaps that cover aspects of energy related to materials being used; these have been summarised in the chapter on Materials and Chemical Processes. However, where there is more than a passing mention of energy considerations the energy aspects are summarised in this chapter.

GENERAL

Nanotechnology helps solve the World's Energy Problems

The European Nanotechnology Gateway, Nanoforum.org, produced a report on nanotechnology and energy in April 2004 (1). It is still a good reference report, and covers all aspects of how nanotechnology will influence developments for all forms of energy, and includes production, storage and distribution.

A European Technology Platform for Sustainable Chemistry – Materials Technology – SusChem

SusChem, the European Technology Platform for Sustainable Chemistry has produced (2005) a strategic research agenda, in draft form (2). Development priorities are listed as:

- Fundamental understanding of structure property relationships
- Computational materials science
- Development of analytical techniques
- From laboratory synthesis to large scale manufacturing.

The report reviews materials for certain sectors and novel coatings features in three of those listed. Although they are not specified as nano-coatings, it is clear, from the emphasis on nanotechnology in the report, that most new coatings can be regarded as nano-based materials.

- Energy management
  - *Self-cleaning, long-lasting coatings with high scratch resistance and weatherability*
- Enhancement of quality for life
  - *Smart surfaces that respond to external stimuli*
- Citizen protection
  - *New functional coatings, e.g. on vehicles that reduce air resistance (or water resistance).*

The energy problem is described as shown below:

Energy Creation – includes current technologies from fossil fuels, alternative technologies from renewable resources, such as solar, hydro, wind, geothermal, biomass and bio-refinery, and nuclear. For materials technology, the focus is on fuel cell technology and photovoltaics.

Energy Transmission and Distribution – includes heat networks, electric wire, and electric grids

Energy Storage – batteries, superconductors, hydrogen

Energy Management – insulation of buildings, more efficient lighting, lighter materials for transport, minimisation of energy losses, etc.

An area of considerable benefit is quoted as:

> *"One significant contribution to modern life would be the development of long-lasting coatings with high scratch resistance and weatherability, smart functional packaging materials, and even self-cleaning and self healing properties. Such surfaces can easily be cleaned by rain, and have a mechanism to self-repair after any surface damage."*

In the section on Materials for Energy Management a 'Products Roadmap for Energy' is drawn up as seen in the figure opposite.

170

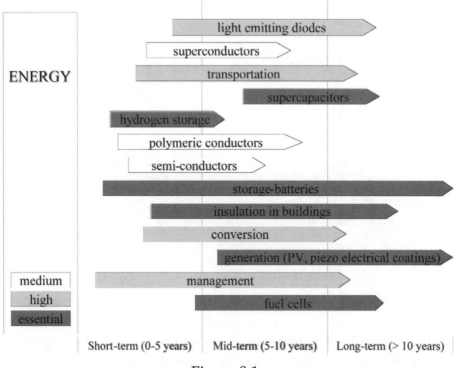

Figure 8.1

European Commission Energy Roadmap Report

The Nanoroadmap Project (NRM) of the European Commission has also produced four energy roadmaps in the following topics:

- Batteries and supercapacitors
- Thermoelectricity
- Solar cells
- Heat insulation / conductance.

All the roadmaps completed to date, in materials, healthcare, and energy, may be freely accessed (3).

For each of the energy ones, the format is the same with a final diagram showing the basic research that is underway with the tech-

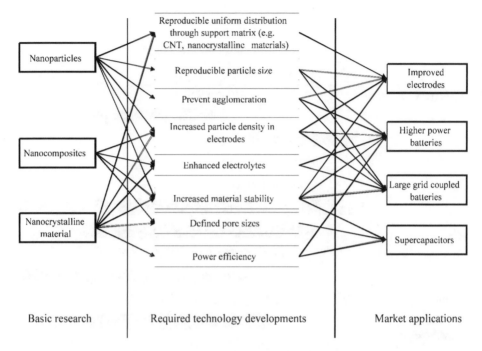

Figure 8.2. Basic research underway with the technology developments required to achieve the desirable applications

nology developments required to achieve the desirable applications. By way of example, the one for rechargeable batteries and supercapacitors is reproduced in Figure 8.2.

European Strategy for Nanotechnology
The European Nanotechnology Gateway (4) prepared the European Strategy for Nanotechnology and subsequently (December 2004) published the outcome of extensive open consultation with a great many groups.

Under the section on energy, the report predicts that nanotechnology will have a major impact on the following:

- Efficient lighting
- Fuel cells

- Batteries
- Thermo-electric sources
- Photovoltaic sources
- Hydrogen motors
- Energy storage
- Hydrogen storage.

National Energy Technology Laboratory – Materials Development

The National Energy Technology Laboratory (NETL) is the only US national laboratory devoted to fossil energy technology. In its forward-look programme it is looking at its materials needs (5).

The focus is on:

- Structural ceramics
- New alloys and coatings
- Functional materials
- Corrosion abatement
- Technology development and transfer.

There is a lot more specific information available on the web site, but the Advanced Research Materials Program Roadmap, designed to develop the materials capability to incorporate components into advanced coal-fuelled plants when they are needed, is shown below.

The technology transition timelines are also given.

Materials Health - Electric Power Research Institute

The Electric Power Research Institute (EPRI) in the States has produced a report (6), that looks at materials use, with a view of enhancing performance and optimising reliability and lifetime for critical systems and components. Topics being assessed are:

- Condition and remaining life assessment
- Aqueous corrosion and protection
- High temperature corrosion and protection
- Advanced materials and material-related topics.

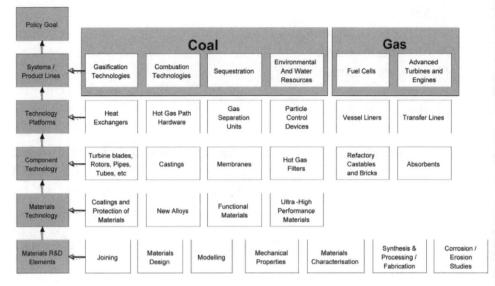

Figure 8.3

The *Electricity Technology Roadmap* that will be produced will have the following goals:

- Accelerate economic growth and productivity
- Resolve the energy / carbon conflict
- Meet the global sustainability challenge.

Materials Powering Europe – MaterialsEuroRoads
Under the MaterialsEuroRoads programme within the EU's Sixth Framework Programme, three roadmaps have been produced and the first was on energy and was entitled "Materials Powering Europe" which was published (7) in April 2006. The comments and research priorities for *Materials for Energy Efficiency* were:

- Innovative coatings technology is an essential way to improve efficiency, for stationary turbine components as well as rotating parts
- High temperature alloy development

- New battery storage materials are needed in order to improve storage
- Heat losses are currently far too high. Waste heat must be used much more efficiently
- Multi-scale modelling in materials technology should be progressed to reduce timescale from an idea to conception. A database to help this should be provided
- There is a great deal of scope to improve communications and networking between all interested parties. This would help inform governments. It would also enable transfer of information across the different sectors of the Energy Industry where some of the problems and issues are common
- The community working on materials topics on fossil plants should communicate with those in nuclear
- Emission free fossil fuel power plants are a requirement. Better public perception of the issues should be provided. Oxygen separation membranes and associated corrosion problems need to be addressed, and re-use of strategic materials and gas emissions should be undertaken
- A strategic plan for material supply is needed, along with new materials concepts for energy storage
- Scale up / integration / implementation from lab to production of intelligent systems is required
- There is an identified need for new sealing and joining systems, with smart, reactive coatings
- Regulatory / fiscal incentives for the production of CO_2 free energy are imperative.

and for *Materials for Sustainable Energy Technologies* comments and research priorities were:

- Mass production would be most beneficial to bringing the costs down for alternative sources of energy generation
- Better storage and transport of energy should be sought. It

is recommended that improvements in superconductors and micro-turbines for distributed generation should be examined. In addition, advances in high energy density storage are needed

- Current funding is channelled towards 'political' topics; real issues that will help Europe should be followed, and less risk aversion would enable step-leaps in progress
- The aim should be to produce materials that can withstand 2000°C, and other extreme conditions
- Costs are currently too high for new systems to be competitive. Functional materials that are highly efficient and are available on a large scale are a requirement. Coatings need to last much longer, and fuel-flexible plants should be explored
- There are few incentives for the provider, or user, of energy to change from current supplies. Energy legislation or tax concessions should be considered for the introduction of new ways of energy generation.

HYDROGEN AND FUEL CELLS

National Hydrogen Energy Roadmap
The United States Department of Energy produced a roadmap for hydrogen energy in November 2002 (8). The reports findings are divided into:

- Production
- Delivery
- Storage
- Conversion
- Applications,

and advanced materials is a key factor in proposed R&D programmes to reduce costs and improve performance, especially in the section on storage.

Canadian Fuel Cell Commercialisation Roadmap

The Canadian Fuel Cell Commercialization Roadmap is an industry-led planning process supported by the Government of Canada and facilitated by Industry Canada, which produced the report in 2003 (9). The potential market for fuel cells and related products is enormous. Global demand is projected to reach $46 billion by 2011 and the potential for 2021 could exceed $2.6 trillion.

The roadmap is not particularly technical, but sets about getting the right infrastructure to take things forward more rapidly with collaborative effort to:

- Develop a national fuel cell strategy which reflects the collaborative commitment of all key stakeholders
- Identify key stakeholder champions who will continually promote the Canadian fuel cell industry

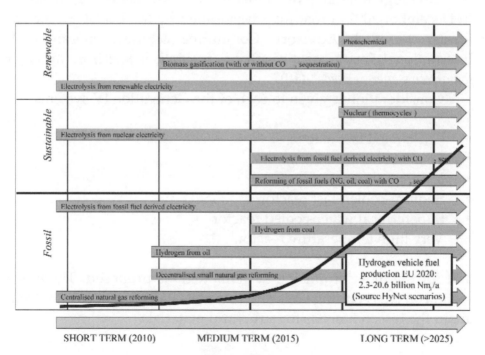

Figure 8.4

- Educate government and other early users as to the long-term benefits of fuel cells and why they should demon-strate/purchase fuel cell products
- Support research and development, product development and early market products.

On the Way Towards a European Hydrogen Energy Roadmap
HyNet have helped produce a European Hydrogen Energy Roadmap. Highlights were published in 2004, and the document is being continually updated. Figure 8.4 shows the timeline for hydrogen production technologies, where the arrows depict the expected earliest commercial introduction of each path.

NUCLEAR

A Technology Roadmap for Generation IV Nuclear Energy Systems
In December 2002, a roadmap was issued by the US DOE Nuclear Energy Research Advisory Committee & the Generation IV International Forum, as a result of *"ten nations preparing today for tomorrow's energy needs"* (10).
Consideration is given to each of the Generation IV systems:

- Gas-cooled fast reactor
- Lead-cooled fast reactor
- Molten salt reactor
- Sodium-cooled fast reactor
- Supercritical water-cooled reactor
- Very high temperature reactor,

and for the most promising systems R&D is proposed. There is a section on cross-cutting fuels and materials R&D that goes into detail about the research needs for structural materials.

PHOTOVOLTAICS

US Photovoltaics Industry – PV Technology Roadmap
In September 1999, technology and market experts from the PV industry, universities, and government research programs were brought together to produce this early roadmap. It identified high priority research and technology transfer needs for the PV Industry at that time. Today many of the proposals have been carried out, and parts of the report are quite out-dated (11).

A Strategic Research Agenda for Photovoltaic Technology
In November 2006, Lithuania issued a strategic research agenda to support its vision for photovaltaic technology (12). For the coming decade, the EU set a target of 3GWp installed photovoltaic capacity, with focus on reducing the cost of PV modules. A problem is the shortage of raw material silicon for solar cells production.

The main short to medium term goal for Lithuania is to be able to produce solar grade silicon, and the longer term vision is to develop new PV technologies.

A Roadmap for Photovoltaics Research in the UK
The UK Energy Research Centre (UKERC) produced a roadmap in August 2007 (13). It covers PV materials, cell and module design and manufacture and applications. It is specific to the UK and reflects the strengths and weaknesses of the research base in the UK, although it is compatible with the roadmaps of other countries, particularly the one recently developed for the European Community. Its primary aim is to identify priority areas for UK PV research and assist the research funding agencies, in developing their research programmes, but it also considers the need to develop UK capacity, both in terms of expertise and research facilities. The roadmap has also been subject to international peer review.

Crystalline silicon and a number of thin film technologies are already well developed and commercially available and as a result much of the immediate research is concerned with issues relevant to manufacturing. Two avenues to silicon cost reduction can be distinguished: reduced silicon consumption per Watt peak (Wp) and reduced silicon cost per kg, and ways of approaching these are recorded.

In contrast, for the advanced devices such as polymer cells, the immediate priorities are for research to provide stable and efficient cells. The driver for all thin film technologies is their potential to achieve large scale and high throughput PV module production at low manufacturing costs. The ultimate success in achieving such a goal lies in the capability to understand the basic material and device properties, fabricate, evaluate and optimise solar cells in the laboratory, and subsequently design and develop the required processes for large-scale production.

The report also contains a section on novel excitonic devices (both dye cells and polymer cells), quantum wells and quantum dots for improved photon capture and conversion and concentrator systems.

A Strategic Research Agenda for Photovoltaic Solar Energy Technology

In 2007 the EU produced a Strategic Research Agenda for PVs (14). Table 8.1 summarises the key targets.

To reach these targets, the report details the R&D issues related to:

Table 8.1

Time-scale:	1980	Today	2015	2030	Long-term
Typical turn-key system price (2006 €/Wp, excl. VAT)	> 30	5	2.5	1	0.5
Typical electricity generation costs Southern Europe (2006 €/kWh)	> 2	0.30	0.15	0.06	0.03
Typical commercial flat-plate module efficiencies	up to 8%	up to 15%	up to 20%	up to 25%	up to 40%
Typical commercial concentrator module efficiencies	(~10%)	up to 25%	up to 30%	up to 40%	up to 60%
Typical system energy pay-back time Southern Europe (years)	> 10	2	1	0.5	0.25

- PV cells and modules:
  - materials
  - conversion principles and devices
  - processing and assembly (including equipment)
- Balance of System (BoS):
  - system components and installation
  - materials installation
  - operation and maintenance
- Concentrator systems
- Environmental quality
- Applicability
- Socio-economic aspects of PV.

The photovoltaics market is estimated to rise to $50 billion by 2009; with key devices being quantum dots (III-V based solar cells).

WIND

The US Small Wind Turbine (SWT) Industry Roadmap
The American Wind Energy Association (AWEA) produced a roadmap in July 2002 (15). Near term (0 to 3 years) actions were:

- Reduce costs by new turbine development activity for low wind speed sites and new component development for SWT
- Research reliability concerns such as lightning, corrosion, bearing lubrication, alternator winding insulation, electronics
- Continue focused long-term research unique to SWT - furling, durability, blade aerodynamics, noise, and power electronics
- Develop packages with other distributed generation and storage technologies.

Mid-Term (4 to 10 years) actions were:

- Work to improve the reliability and reduce the cost of power electronics
- Work to eliminate noise from small turbine designs
- Develop consumer-friendly performance predictions
- Improve analytical design tools
- Continue the development of packages with other distributed generation and storage technologies.

For long term (11 years +):

- Develop hydrogen-based systems
- Develop blackout protection strategies
- Establish links with storage and other power technologies

Prioritising Wind Energy Research

In July 2005, a European Strategic Research Agenda has been produced by the Wind Energy Sector (16). The main points, described as 'showstoppers', included:

- In terms of resource estimation: maximum availability of wind resource data, in the public domain where possible, to ensure that financiers, insurers and project developers can develop high quality projects efficiently, avoiding project failure through inaccurate data.
- With regard to wind turbines: the availability of robust, low-maintenance offshore turbines, as well as research into the development of increased reliability and availability of offshore turbines.
- For wind farms: the research and development of wind farm level storage systems.
- In terms of grid integration: planning and design processes for a trans-European grid, with sufficient connection points to serve future large scale wind power plants. This task should be undertaken by the wider energy sector in close cooperation with the wind energy sector.
- With regard to environment and public support: a

European communication strategy for the demonstration of research results on the effects of large-scale wind power plants on ecological systems, targeted at the general public and policy makers. To include specific recommendations for wind park design and planning practices.

Strategic Research Agenda – Market Deployment Strategy for Wind Energy

In July 2008, the European Wind Energy Technology Platform produced a roadmap to provide a market deployment strategy for wind energy (17). Wind energy could cover 12-14% of the EU's electricity consumption by 2020, with a total installed capacity of 180 GW. This could increase to 22-28% of consumption and 300 GW in 2030.

The aim of the research priorities is to ensure that, by 2030, wind energy will be the most cost efficient energy source on the market, which can only be achieved by developing technology that enables the European industry to deliver highly cost-efficient wind turbines. The focus is on large-scale integration of wind power. The goal is to enable high penetration levels with low integration costs, while maintaining system reliability.

RENEWABLES AND CAPTURE

Renewable Energy Technology Roadmap

In October 2002, a renewable energy roadmap was produced by the Australian Government (18). For the purposes of the analysis, the Australian renewable energy industry has been broadly classified into ten technology sectors:

- Biomass energy
- Cogeneration
- Enabling technologies
- Fuel cells and hydrogen fuels
- Geothermal energy

- Hydro-electricity, tidal energy and wave energy
- Photovoltaics (PV)
- Remote area power supply (RAPS)
- Solar thermal energy
- Wind energy.

For each technology sector, the roadmap identifies a number of actions that will allow the technologies and products to better meet market needs.

Innovation Roadmap on Bio-based Feedstocks, Fuels, and Industrial Products

BioProducts Canada, in 2004, produced a roadmap for bio-based feedstocks, fuels, and industrial processes (19). Targets were set for greater production and use of biofuels:

1 Increase production of alternative fuels that help reduce greenhouse gases (Canada currently produces 240 million litres of ethanol).
2 Increase the output of biodiesel and biodiesel blends to reduce airborne emissions.
3 Improve the cost competitiveness of producing biofuels by:
    - utilizing high-end molecules in feedstocks to produce valuable by-products to defray energy costs
    - adopting cogeneration practices to fully utilize all fuels and all heat generated in production processes
    - minimizing heat requirements in production processes through catalysis, enzymes and innovative membranes
    - reducing biomass transportation costs through bundling or compacting, or by treating residues and using them in close proximity to the resource
    - supporting and integrating the disparate sciences.
4 Encourage the growth of research and development in biofuels and industrial products, similar to the level achieved in fossil fuels.

Carbon Dioxide Capture and Storage – A Technology Roadmap
In January 2004, Australia produced a roadmap on Carbon Dioxide Capture and Storage (20). The appendices in the report contain details on:

- Post combustion
- Transport CO_2 to storage site and condition CO_2
- Safely inject CO_2
- Conversion / re-use of CO_2 for value added products
- Ameliorate environmental concerns.

Future Fuels for the APEC Region
In September 2005, an APEC collaborative initiative, between the APEC Energy Working Group and the APEC Industrial Science and Technology Working Group produced a roadmap for Future Fuels (21). It was coordinated jointly by the APEC Center for Technology Foresight in Thailand and the Office of the National Science Advisor in Canada and sponsored by Canada, Chinese Taipei and Thailand supplemented by APEC central funds. The roadmap explores future fuel options by focusing on three future fuel options and exploring their interaction over the time period 2005-2030:

- Unconventional hydrocarbons
- Biofuels
- Hydrogen.

Towards a Technology Roadmap for Canadian Forest Biorefineries
In 2006, Industry Canada sponsored a roadmapping exercise for Canadian forest biorefineries (22). A wide range of opportunities for pulp and paper mills to produce alternate products in collaboration with chemical and energy industries were identified. The objective was to commercialise these technologies and adopt them into existing operations. With this experience, the development of integrated, stand-alone forest biorefineries would begin to evolve. A technology roadmap was seen as an ideal vehicle to bring the academic, industry,

research and government communities together to develop further the concept of forest biorefineries and research priorities.

Canada's Carbon Dioxide Capture and Storage Technology Roadmap

In March 2006, the Canadians produced a technology roadmap covering carbon dioxide capture and storage (CCS) (23). For the way forward it was recognised that the following were required:

- Policy and regulatory frameworks
- Public outreach and education
- Technology watch and international collaboration
- Science and technology R&D
- Demonstration
- National coordination.

The report is comprehensive and has a great deal of statistics relevant to Canada.

REFERENCES

Some of the roadmaps referenced here may be obtained in hard copy from the organisations producing them, but the easiest way to access them is through the web references, which are given below. Should hard copies be required, then they can be printed off, or these same references may help with providing the right contacts to approach for paper copies. However, as time progresses, web sites go through changes, so some of the references may fall out of date. In these cases, it is suggested that the title of the roadmap is fed into a search engine, to determine if the roadmap is still available.

1   Nanoforum.org report on world energy problems
     http://www.nanoforum.org/nf06~modul~showmore~folder~99999~
     scid~121~.html?action=longview_publication&
2   SRA from the European Technology Platform for Sustainable Chemistry

http://www.suschem.org/media.php?mId=2678

3   EU Nanoroadmap project report on energy
    http://www.nanoroadmaps.it

4   Nanoforum.org report on a European Strategy for Nanotechnology
    http://www.nanoforum.org

5   US National Energy Technology Laboratory roadmap
    http://www.netl.doe.gov/technologies/coalpower/advresearch/
    material_pages/index.html

6   Electric Power Research Institute roadmap for materials development
    http://www.epri.com/targetSSTContent.asp?program=236618&value=
    01TSST501&objid=266790

7   European SMART Consortium, *Materials powering Europe*
    http://www.smart-ssa.net/datapool/page/9/Proceedings_Energy.pdf

8   US Department of Energy Hydrogen Energy Roadmap
    http://www.hydrogen.energy.gov/pdfs/national_h2_roadmap.pdf

9   Industry Canada Fuel Cell Commercialization Roadmap
    http://www.hydrogeneconomy.gc.ca/docs/roadmap_e.pdf

10 US Technology Roadmap for Generation IV Nuclear Energy Systems
    http://gif.inel.gov/roadmap/pdfs/gen_iv_roadmap.pdf

11 http://www.hubbertpeak.com/apollo2/photovoltaics/
    PVIndustryRoadmap.pdf

12 Lithuanian SRA for photovoltaics
    http://www.protechnology.lt/docs/PV-SRA.pdf

13 UK Energy Research Centre (UKERC) roadmap on photovoltaics
    http://ukerc.rl.ac.uk/Roadmaps/A_Road_Map_for_Photovoltaics_
    Research_in_the_UK.pdf

14 SRA form the EU's Technology Platform for Photovoltaics
    http://cordis.europa.eu/technology-platforms/pdf/photovoltaics.pdf

15 American Wind Energy Association roadmap for small wind turbines
    http://www.awea.org/smallwind/documents/31958.pdf

16 SRA from the Europe's wind energy sector
    http://www.windplatform.eu/fileadmin/ewetp_docs/Structure/
    SRA_final.pdf

17 SRA from the European Technology Platform for Wind Energy
    http://www.ewea.org/index.php?id=60&no_cache=1&tx_ttnews
    %5Btt_news%5D=1361&tx_ttnews%5BbackPid%5D=1&cHash=a082035a00

18 Australian Government report on their renewable energy industry
    http://www.ret.gov.au/Industry/RenewableEnergy/Pages/default.aspx

19 Canadian roadmap for bio-based feedstocks, fuels, and industrial processes
    http://www.ic.gc.ca/epic/site/trm-crt.nsf/en/rm00114e.html

20 Australia roadmap on Carbon Dioxide Capture and Storage

https://extra.co2crc.com.au/modules/pts2/download.php?file_id=591 &rec_id=89

21   APEC roadmap for future fuels
      http://www.ic.gc.ca/.../vwapj/future_fuelscarburants_avenir_eng.pdf/ $file/future_fuels-carburants_avenir_eng.pdf

22   Industry Canada roadmap for Canadian forest biorefineries
      http://www.ic.gc.ca/epic/site/lsg-pdsv.nsf/vwapj/Biorefineries-eng.pdf/ $FILE/Biorefineries-eng.pdf

23   Canadian roadmap for carbon dioxide capture and storage
      http://www.nrcan.gc.ca/es/etb/cetc/combustion/co2trm/htmldocs/ ccstrm_doc_e.html

CHAPTER 9

ROADMAPS IN CONSUMER PRODUCTS

CONTENTS

BACKGROUND

There are a limited number of technology roadmaps and related reports which address the field of consumer products. However, in such a competitive area the authors recognise that many companies have carried out roadmaps for internal use on many products e.g. toothpastes, under-arm deodorants, aerosol sprays, etc.

Also in this section, a number of roadmaps have been summarised in relation to water technologies, and for the food and drink sector.

ROADMAPS

Desalination and Water Purification Technology Roadmap

The US Bureau of Reclamation and the Sandia National Laboratories produced a roadmap in January 2003 on Desalination and Water Purification (1). Conventional desalination processes are also very effective in removing contaminants from impaired water, but their drawback is cost.

Research identified in the roadmap is expected to:

- Reduce capital and operating costs of existing and future technologies
- Increase operational efficiency
- Expand contaminant-removal capabilities.

The main technologies to be addressed are:

- Membrane Technologies - technologies that desalinate and purify water by pushing it through a semi-permeable membrane thereby removing contaminants
- Alternative Technologies - technologies that take advantage of non-traditional methods
- Thermal Technologies - technologies relying on boiling or

freezing water and then capturing the purified water while the contaminants remain behind
- Concentrate Management Technologies - technologies which consider the disposal, volumetric reduction, and beneficial use of the primary by-product of desalination
- Reuse/Recycling Technologies - often membrane or alternative technologies that must be designed to handle increased contaminant loads due to their post-consumer application.

Technical Textiles Technology Roadmap
Technitex Faraday Partnership was established to add focus to the UK's technical textiles interests. These are for high-value textiles in transportation (including automotive), marine and aerospace, personal protective equipment (PPE), medical, construction / agriculture, sportswear and outdoor clothing, and interiors. A roadmap for the sector was produced in 2004 (2), but it is not available electronically.

There is emphasis on new materials such as synthetics, bio-fibres, conductive fibres, nanomaterials and regenerated wool. 'Smart textiles' are highlighted, and enhanced late-stage design and colouration are featured. Sensors, actuators, and flexible logic circuits are also expected to influence new products in this sector.

Industry Canada is producing a roadmap for its textiles sector, but it has not yet been published (3).

International Roadmap for Consumer Packaging: Exploring the Strategic Landscape of the Packaging Sector
In January 2006, the Institute of Manufacturing produced an International Roadmap for Consumer Packaging for the next 10 years (4), which was the result of 12 workshops, attended by 200 delegates, representing experts from 70 different organisations, over a three year period. The priority themes, which have a very strong market pull are shown in the Table 9.1.

Table 9.1

Market and business themes	Product performance themes	Technology themes	Resource themes
• Ageing population • Changing household structures • Increasing demand for information • Convenience • Needs of the individual • Health • Safety • Environmental concern • Internet-related opportunities • Increasing regulation • Opportunities in new markets • Drive to lower costs • Manufacturing offshore	• Waste minimisation • Recycling • Biodegradability • Opening / closing • Convenience in use • New retail channels • Counterfeiting • Traceability • Materials	• RFID • Nanotechnology • Intelligent packaging • Advances in production	• Partnerships

The Future is Textiles! - Strategic Research Agenda
The European Technology Platform for the Future of Textiles and Clothing produced an SRA in June 2006 (5). Three major development trends and their research priorities are highlighted:

1 *From Commodities towards Specialties* - new speciality fibres and fibre-composites for innovative textile products, functionalisation of textile materials and related processes, and bio-based materials, biotechnologies and environmentally friendly textile processing
2 *New Textile Applications* – scientific / technological solutions enabling new textile products for improved human performance, new textile products for innovative technical applications and smart textiles and clothing
3 *Towards Customisation* - mass customisation for clothing and fashion, new design and product development concepts and technologies, and integrated quality and life cycle management concepts.

192

Nanotechnology in Consumer Products

Nanoforum.org, the European Nanotechnology Gateway, produced a report (6) in October 2006 specifically for consumer products, which was not so much a roadmap, but more a review of the current situation, with some speculation about the future. The report looks at the effects different nano-structures can have and lists all the property changes that can be achieved through interfacial effects, before going on to discuss quantum mechanical effects.

Many products are considered under the headings: textiles and apparel, care products, consumer electronics, sports, home improvement, and household products. Finally, there is speculation that future high impact developments will be based on the small size and the electronic properties of nano-enabled products.

Strategic Research Agenda – Water Research: A Necessary Investment In Our Common Future

In October 2006, the EU's Water Supply and Sanitation Technology Platform produced a Strategic Research Agenda for activities in water research (7). The water sector is facing an alarming evolution because of three main drivers: climate change, an ageing and deteriorating infrastructure, and globalisation and population growth. The report looks at the water sector for both Europe and elsewhere, and identifies four major challenges that need to be addressed:

1   Increasing water stress and water costs – where the traditional solution has been to bring water in from greater distances (the civil engineering solution), but increasingly local water is now being treated (the chemical engineering solution). For the future, there will be more emphasis on conserving water and improving the efficiency of water use (the social engineering approach).
2   Urbanisation – with the move of rural inhabitants to cities, the burden on the old and deteriorating infrastructure is increasing and it is likely that innovative solutions to water re-use will be required.

3   Extreme events - the effects of climate change, floods and droughts, will need to be tackled in an integrated way.

4   Rural and underdeveloped areas – there are many out-lying areas in Europe which do not have a significant infrastructure for water services. It is estimated that 10% of the European population receives water from very small supplies which do not meet European drinking water standards. Affordable and manageable point of use water supplies are needed and such technologies will have export potential to developing countries.

Smart and Active Packaging to Reduce Food Waste

The Smart.mat section of the UK's Materials Knowledge Transfer Network produced a report in November 2006 (8) on smart and active packaging designed to reduce food wastage. In the UK alone, it is estimated that £20 billion worth of unused food is thrown away every year. A key supply chain technology which is already beginning to address the problem is RFID. This is not just for improving logistics of transfer to the shops, but is likely to provide information on status indication, such as checking storage temperatures have been maintained. As the cost of RFID tags is reduced there will be a dramatic increase in their use.

Improved packaging is also expected to grow, gas permeation and anti-bacterial agents are already being used and further development is anticipated. Track and trace sensors and indicators in the packaging will provide information on detailed storage and transport in order to extend the shelf life of foodstuffs. The emerging range of devices based on 'plastic electronics' will provide dynamic packaging with the possibility of audible and video output, although it is expected that pharmaceutical packaging will lead in this field.

Consumer Packaging – Opportunities for Smart Technologies

February 2007 saw another report from Smart.mat describing opportunities in smart technologies for consumer packaging (9). Packaging has traditionally had three functions: containing the goods, protecting the goods, and providing information about the goods. New materials and packaging design have made significant changes, but so far smart and intelligent features have not made much of an impact in the field of packaging. The report states three drivers that show there is a call for better smart packaging:

1   50% of people do not follow instructions for prescribed medicines
2   the value of counterfeit goods in the world is estimated to be US $1 trillion per annum
3   consumers are showing less brand loyalty.

Two technology types will make a major impact over the next 15 years, and these cut across all types of packaging. The first is storage and retrieval of information through RFID, which is near future, and will additionally prevent counterfeiting and ensure medical compliance. The second technology, printed electronics, is further away, but is expected to revolutionise packaging.

Nanomaterials in Consumer Products
The Economic and Scientific Policy Section of the Policy Department for the European Parliament commissioned a report in April 2007 on nanomaterials in consumer products (10). The focus is on availability on the European market, and gives an inventory of products based on nanomaterials, an analysis of the potential risks associated with those products, and the adequacy of the regulatory framework to address potential risks.

To assess the risks, the authors quite rightly take into account the likely exposure and potential hazards. They comment on the lack of toxicity data for nanomaterials, but are able to categorise products as high or low risk. Potentially high exposures are expected from consumer products containing free nanoparticles with direct exposure to humans of environmental organisms. Examples of these are cleaning and personal care products, and cosmetics. Low exposures are anticipated from nanomaterials which are embedded e.g in computers and electronics, cooking utensils, sporting goods, and coatings.

The safety of consumer products is not regulated by one single piece of legislation, and no relevant regulations mention nanomaterials, but implicitly cover nanomaterials, by making industry responsible for the chemicals or products they produce. However the report concludes by saying that more knowledge is required to assess how well current regulations are at addressing any potential risks.

European Technology Platform on Food for Life

Under the auspices of the Confederation of the Food and Drink Industries of Europe, the European Technology Platform on Food for Life produced, in September 2007, a Strategic Research Agenda for 2007 to 2020 (11). Six research challenges are listed:

1 Ensuring that the healthy choice is the easy choice for consumers
2 Delivering a healthier diet
3 Developing quality food products
4 Assuring safe foods that consumers can trust
5 Achieving sustainable food production
6 Managing the food chain.

In terms of priorities, the main thrusts are:

1 Improve health, well-being and longevity,
2 Build consumer trust in the food chain, and
3 Derive from sustainable and ethical production.

The report highlights the fact that 95% of European food producers are SMEs, and many are not active in R&D. There is therefore a need to improve existing structures to encourage more participation.

REFERENCES

Some of the roadmaps referenced here may be obtained in hard copy from the organisations producing them, but the easiest way to access them is through the web references, which are given below. Should hard copies be required, then they can be printed off, or these same references may help with providing the right contacts to approach for paper copies. However, as time progresses, web sites go through changes, so some of the references may fall out of date. In these cases, it is suggested that the title of the roadmap is fed into a search engine, to determine if the roadmap is still available.

1   Desalination and Water Purification Technology Roadmap
    http://wrri.nmsu.edu/tbndrc/roadmapreport.pdf
2   Byrne,C., *Technical Textiles Technology Roadmap*, TechniTex Faraday
    Partnership, 2004.
3   Industry Canada technology roadmap for textiles
    http://www.ic.gc.ca/epic/site/catp-pictv.nsf/en/td00356e.html
4   International Roadmap for Consumer Packaging
    http://www.ifm.eng.cam.ac.uk/ctm/trm/resources.html (may be
    downloaded from this site)
5   SRA from the European Technology Platform for the Future of Textiles and
    Clothing
    http://www.textile-platform.org/documents/Key%20Documents/SRA/
    TextileETP_SRA_final.pdf
6   Nanoforum.org report on consumer products
    http://www.nanoforum.org/nf06~modul~showmore~folder~99999~
    scid~421~.html?action=longview_publication& (may be downloaded from
    this site)
7   SRA from the EU's Water Supply and Sanitation Technology Platform
    http://www.eugris.info/displayresource.asp?ResourceID=6237&Cat=
    document (may be downloaded from this site)
8   Smart.mat report on smart and active packaging designed to reduce food
    wastage
    http://amf.globalwatchonline.com/epicentric_portal/site/AMF/
    menuitem.f281959d6f4ca28d08a38510eb3e8a0c/?mode=0 (may be down-
    loaded from this site)
9   Smart.mat technology roadmap for consumer packaging
    http://www.faradaypackaging.com/sendfile.php?file=Consumer+

Packaging+for+SMART+technologies.pdf

10   http://www.nanet.nu/.../4%20nanomaterials%20in%20consumer%
     20products_2006.pdf

11   SRA from the European Technology Platform on Food for Life
     http://cordis.europa.eu/technology-platforms/pdf/foodforlife.pdf

CHAPTER 10

ROADMAPPING THE FUTURE

CONTENTS

INTRODUCTION

We journey on a continuously moving line that divides the past and the future. Predicting what is likely to happen in the distant future is the greatest challenge facing us. It is the preoccupation of a group of people called futurologists. There are as many future scenarios available as there are futurologists that predict them. In the book 'Atlas of the Future' (1), edited by Ian Pearson, a futurologist, twenty-five leading experts give a perspective on the future complete with statistical data on the Earth's natural resources and the developments taking place in most of the important spheres of human endeavour. In a later book 'Business 2010: Mapping the New Commercial Landscape' (2) Pearson describes the impact of emergent technologies on future business environments. In his books 'The Age of Spiritual Machines' and 'The Singularity is Near' (3) (4), the futurologist, Ray Kurzwell explores the consequences for society when humans and intelligent machines unite. If this ever happens, then most of the roadmaps for the future will have to be re-written. For now, however this just fuels interesting and intellectual discussion. Sometimes today's fiction can be tomorrow's reality. The advances in computer science, robotics and nanotechnology tend to be leading us in that direction.

Such publications provide speculative input on which to base future trends but do not always take account of unforeseen innovations or new developments that can suddenly change the path of predictions. Innovations are an important element in shaping our future. Just one innovation or an invention can radically disrupt or change a business or even a whole industry in a very short time. It has to be stated, however, that innovation has to be followed by an aggressive implementation process for it to succeed in bringing competitive advantage to the innovator. The past is littered with innovations that have failed through the lack of a supporting implementation plan. Roadmaps do include such plans so they will help the owners of the intellectual property derived from such innovations to benefit commercially.

The living world is a manifest of innovative design. Nanoscale science and technology are now enabling us to understand many of the natural living processes. Studying nanostructures at the cell biology and DNA level gives us insight into the working of these processes. In his book, 'The Extreme Future' (5), James Canton, who is the Chairman of the American Institute for Global Futures, lists eight fundamental innovations that he believes will shape the future. Taken from an American perspective, they are: Biomimetics, Photonics, Nano-biotech, Genomics, Neuro-devices, Nano-energy, Quantum Encryption and Bio-detection. According to a report published in 2008 by the American Society of Mechanical Engineers, ASME (6), nanotechnology and biotechnology will dominate technological development in the next 20 years. The report claims that these technologies will give future engineers the knowledge to solve problems in many diverse fields including medicine, energy, water management, aeronautics, agriculture and environmental management. Having knowledge is essential, but the prerequisite is for society to be made aware of the implications and consequences of applying that knowledge. This is an example where strategic roadmapping becomes important.

Unexpected change can also come from natural or human-made disasters. Epidemics of disease are perhaps the most threatening disaster areas. Air travel makes society more vulnerable to this than in the past when geographical boundaries retarded the spread of virulent plagues. Even with all the current medical knowledge, stopping the spread of an epidemic is a formidable task, particularly if the disease results from a mutant strain that defies existing drugs.

Now in the first decade of the twenty-first century, the rapid rate of progress requires planners and decision-makers to embrace change and to take on challenges and the risks they bring. Gone are the old forecasting methods that relied heavily on past history from which to extrapolate. The new future is going to be different from anything that has gone before. Past knowledge will be useful but change will be driven by technological developments, globalization and the needs of the rapidly emerging economies in Asia.

We live in the information age where unlimited knowledge is available at the press of a button on a keyboard to anyone anywhere. Today over 1 billion people are connected to the Internet. At the end of next decade this is likely to be in excess of 3 billion. This number could increase when the population of China is connected. Decision-makers in Government, industry and business are becoming over-whelmed with information. It can produce a state of disorientation resulting in poor decision-making. This condition was well expounded by Alvin Toffler in his book 'Future Shock' (7) first published in 1970. Strategic roadmapping can help to prevent this condition as it plots a well-planned path to the future, thus reducing the risk and expediting the decision-making process.

In this final chapter of the book we do not wish to take on the role of futurologists or speculators but show what a roadmap to the future could look like by using existing knowledge and trends. We use the methodology described in Chapter 2 by putting down two questions.

Where are we now?

Where are we going?

A PATH TO THE FUTURE

Let us take a snapshot at the present time. What paths do we see before us ? We shall confine our view to the impact that science and technology is having and will continue to have in the coming decades for a number of key areas of human activity.

Society is now reaping the harvest of twentieth century science and technology and the advances they brought about. At the dawn of the twenty-first century the World Wide Web (the Internet) came into common use for the communication and exchange of information. The Internet and its successor to be, the global superhighway, has reduced the significance of geographical boundaries. In the future, nation states may be replaced with cyber communities linked by common interest rather than historical, cultural or political ideology.

Google, the most used software search engine, is replacing reference libraries to give users almost instant access to unlimited information at the press of a button. This instant access to knowledge and information, both past and current, has radically changed the world. The 'global village concept' has become of age. But has this instant access to information made decision-making easier or harder? Without a roadmap that includes all possible scenarios, including commercial ones, then large amounts of information just provides too many options. For example, does a drug company invest many millions on the production of a drug that will cure or arrest a disease in a poor country if the market intelligence shows a loss on its commercial return simply because those in need cannot afford it? It becomes a decision between business, economics and satisfying a human need. The same problem arises for making drugs to combat epidemics that may never happen. Investment decisions will always have a business input. Companies and governments have to make such business decisions on a daily basis, although the latter often take account of voters' needs. Globalisation has increased the complexity of decision-making as instant communications makes it possible to track events as they happen. Increasingly, therefore more sophisticated methods of assessment and evaluation of data are required.

We need first to look at how the world is developing and the key issues that confront the human race. Rapidly growing economies require increased physical resources such as energy, materials, trained workforces, food, water, transport, communications and healthcare. The predicted climate change and its effect on the environment will require greater planning for the future. The clash of cultures, values and ideologies and the threats they bring to security and peace will have to be taken into account in writing a roadmap for the future. In setting out to construct our roadmap we must first examine where we are now in some of the key areas. We shall confine ourselves to just three: Energy, Transport, Medicine and Healthcare. Roadmaps covering other sectors in the earlier chapters showed that in a global context there are common and related links. For example, the impact of new materials is generic to developments in almost every sector. Nanotechnology has an important role in the evolution of such materials.

ENERGY SUPPLY

General
The future of civilization hinges on a sustainable supply of energy. Steam energy was the driver of the first industrial revolution in the nineteenth century. But it was technological developments, mainly in engineering, that made the steam engines and machines for the factories on which early industry was founded. Now in the twenty-first century, it is developments in technology that will provide the solutions to the problems that face us in seeking clean, affordable, renewable energy supplies. In the long term these are essential to sustain civilisation in a world with a growing population, estimated to be about 10 billion by 2050.

Almost every sector of industry requires a continuous energy supply. Demand for energy is increasing while the supply of fossil fuel sources, oil, gas and coal will in the long term diminish, forcing the nations who own these assets to increase the price. For example, America currently imports 70% of its oil at a cost of $700 billion a year. At the time of writing, oil price rises are having a serious affect on the economies of nations and the growth of the global economy. The International Energy Agency predicts that, by 2030, overall energy demand will increase 55% from today's levels. With this there is an associated requirement for $22 trillion of new infrastructure projects. A large part of this increase will have to come from alternative renewable sources. The need to cut carbon emissions to reduce global warming also places urgent demands to secure these sources.

The range of energy roadmaps shown in Chapter 8 clearly indicates the range of advanced technologies now being applied to solve the problems of alternative energy supplies. They cover the current status of technologies for renewable energy supplies and the timescales when they are likely to become economically viable.

A comprehensive assessment of alternative energy supplies was given in a book edited by James Winebrake in 2003 (8). The European Union revised their earlier estimates on the renewable energy required to meet targets for energy demand in Europe. These were published in their '*Renewable Energy Technology Roadmap 2020*' (9). The current expectation is that the overall contribution of renewable energy to the energy supply in 2020 is about 21%. These estimates are based on a conservative annual growth scenario for the different technologies and make an assumption about energy uptake between 2010 and 2020. The urgency of global sustainability of energy supply is driving technological developments at a higher rate with huge investments being made in nuclear, solar and wind power systems. Developing these is being given top priority by most industrial nations. But while existing sources like coal are still viable, with some countries having large stocks, there is little incentive for such countries to seek alternatives. This fact has to be considered when forming future energy policies in a global context.

Coal is still the most abundant fuel with several hundred years' worth of recoverable supplies left on the planet but until sequestration processes for carbon dioxide emission are established to make coal a clean source, it will remain the least desirable fuel owing to its high carbon dioxide emission when burnt. China has large coal reserves and its growing industrial economy is thirsty for low cost power. It is currently building a 500 MW coal-fired power station every week. This trend must be reversed otherwise global warming will not be retarded. A number of alternative energy supplies to fossil fuels; include nuclear power, solar power, hydrogen, wind and wave power. The world energy demand for the twenty-first century was presented at the International Geological Congress in Washington DC in 1985 (10). See the predictions in Figure 10.1.

The key alternatives for the future are reviewed below.

Nuclear Power
Nuclear power is a well-established clean technology. It currently

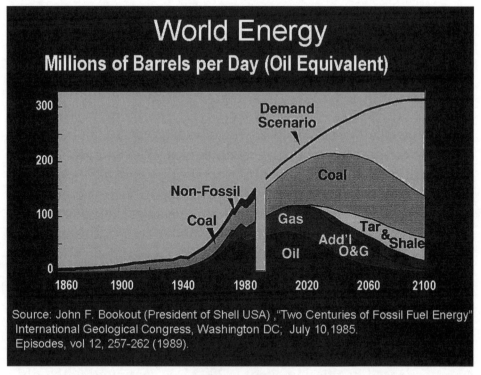

Figure 10.1

supplies about 6% of the world's energy needs and 15% of electricity from 439 nuclear reactors. The US, Japan and Europe combined account for 56.5% of this value. It is mainly the advanced countries that derive their electricity requirements from this source. For example, the US has 104 operational power reactors that supply about 19% of it power needs. France has the highest usage with 78% from 59 plants and the UK with 18% from 23 plants on 9 sites.

Nuclear power came to the fore in the late 1950s and 1960s, with the building of many nuclear power stations around the world. However, the hazards associated with the disposal of nuclear waste have always been, for environmentalists, an argument against nuclear power. Combined with the Chernobyl and Three Mile Island accidents in the 1980s and the availability of cheap oil and gas, the nuclear industry went into decline in the 1990s in some countries and ironically in America and Britain who pioneered its development. Now, in 2008, although there are only 439 nuclear power reactors in operation worldwide, the number is expected to grow significantly in the coming decades. We are about to see a renaissance of interest in the use of nuclear power around the world (11). Since the Chernobyl and Three Mile Island accidents there have been advances in operational safety systems and supporting technologies. For example, the new 'Generation III' designs are simple to operate and have advanced passive safety features that rely on physical forces such as gravity and convection, with little or no need for mechanical devices such as pumps, the cause of some early problems. A significant feature of these new designs is that the volume of waste generated per kilowatt-hour output will be much less than in the older ones and they will deliver double the amount of electricity over a 60 year lifetime.

The key physics that makes nuclear power such a formidable power source is the huge amounts of energy that can be derived from a small quantity of Uranium-235. At the atomic level, the thermal energy released in a fission event is 200 MeV, compared with only a few electron-volts (ev) produced each time a hydrocarbon molecule is broken by burning carbon-based fuels. As a result, a single nuclear-reactor fuel pellet just one cm long can produce the same amount of electricity as 5 tons of coal. Reactors produce tiny amounts of waste, as opposed to the vast volumes of pollutants pumped unchecked into the environment by the burning of coal or oil. Although nuclear waste is much more toxic than these pollutants, it can be completely contained. During the last decade, materials technology has advanced enough to provide the necessary knowledge to solve the containment problem. Producing huge amounts of energy without any greenhouse gases, nuclear power has a pivotal role in combating global warming.

The economics of electricity generation from nuclear reactors depends on having a suitable supporting infrastructure such as possession of the technology for supply and safe operation of plants, fuel reprocessing and waste disposal facilities and environmentally acceptable disposal sites.

Solar Power

About 165,000 terawatts of solar energy from the sun constantly hits the earth but most of it cannot be collected instantly, only indirectly over a period of time. In one hour the Sun delivers the same amount of energy as consumed by humanity in one year and in 36 hours releases as much energy as exists in all the Earth's oil reserves (12). Solar energy is inexhaustible so therefore should be our main source. The problems are cost, conversion efficiency, storage and availability, compared to other renewable sources. The cost of building and maintaining huge numbers of solar panels in areas of continuous sunlight is enormous. The current global consumption of energy is at a rate of 13 terawatts (TW) and with population growth and economic expansion this could increase to 45 TW by 2050. For this to be a practical, principal energy source, the efficiency of solar cells would have to increase much beyond 20%.

It is estimated that due to technical developments in photovoltaic cells the current costs of $0.30 per kilowatt hour (KWh) could be reduced to $0.02 per KWh within 20 years. The first generation of cells based on single crystals of silicon, commonly used, have conversion efficiencies of about 18%. New developments in silicon thin film technologies and other materials have reduced manufacturing costs but not significantly increased efficiencies. Recent developments in nanotechnology could reduce the cost of solar cell production by improving the efficiency of thin films and other materials.

Scientists from Spectrolab, Inc., a subsidiary of Boeing in the US, have recently published their research on the fabrication of solar cells that surpass the 40% efficiency milestone-the highest efficiency achieved for any photovoltaic device (13) (14). Most conventional solar cells used in today's applications, such as for supplemental power for homes and buildings, are single-junction silicon cells that have optimal efficiency for a relatively narrow range of photon energies.

Nanotechnology gave birth to quantum dots, now being used as biological and chemical markers in many diverse applications. It has been shown that solar cells based on quantum dots could theoretically convert more than 65% of the Sun's energy into electricity, approximately doubling the efficiency of solar cells (15). Quantum well solar cells (16) are now being researched for use as solar energy converters as the heat losses in conversion are absent, so giving advantages over conventional solar converters. So far in the laboratory these have produced conversion efficiencies of 27%.

Solar panels are the main source of power for space vehicles and orbiting stations and satellites since they can operate efficiently in a space environment. Now many research laboratories and companies are investing heavily in solar cell and solar panel developments for use on Earth.

It has been estimated that globally installed capacity of solar power systems could reach 259 GW by 2020, delivering an estimated power of 325 TW, corresponding to approximately 1.8% of the total electricity consumption. By 2040, this could rise to be 16% to the world's electricity output. Then photovoltaic solar power will become an established world energy source. It is likely that due to the energy crisis, these expectations will be exceeded in a much shorter timescale.

Recently it was announced by Pacific Gas & Electric of California in America that two photovoltaic power plants will be built in California with 800 megawatts peak generating capacity (17). These are approximately equal to the size of a large coal-burning power plant or a small nuclear plant, and should generate twelve times as much electricity as the largest plant operating today and demonstrate that solar energy will achieve significant scale. Other California Companies, OptiSolar, and SunPower are also building large scale plants that will generate about 550 and 250 megawatts respectively. These are just some examples of the leap forward in scale taken by solar energy companies. As photovoltaic technology develops, similar investments can be expected in other countries.

The Hydrogen Economy
'I believe that one day water will be used as a fuel — that the hydrogen and the oxygen which constitute it, separately or simul-

taneously, will provide an inexhaustible source of heat and light of an intensity unknown to petroleum. One day, instead of being fired with coal, steamships and locomotives will be propelled by these two compressed gases, which will burn in their engines with enormous energy. Thus there is nothing to fear. As long as the earth is inhabited it shall provide for the needs of its inhabitants, and they will never want for light or heat. Water is the coal of the future'.

Jules Verne, The Mysterious Island, 1874 (18).

Now in the twenty-first century the prediction Jules Verne made in his book is about to become reality. Alongside solar power, hydrogen is most likely to be a future energy source since it has the highest energy content per unit weight of any known fuel. It is abundant, clean and secure, being available to everyone. The main problems are that it does not occur naturally without attachment to other elements like oxygen or carbon and is costly to separate and transfer into fuel cells. It is also unstable and needs to be controlled. Currently natural gas provides 90% of the hydrogen made in the world today. But gas is becoming more scarce and costly. Governments and all the main energy supply companies are investing billions of dollars in research and development. It is estimated that by 2030, hydrogen will be a viable alternative to oil and gas.

Hydrogen Generation and Storage

Hydrogen is an energy carrier so a sustainable method of hydrogen generation will be required to realise a sustainable hydrogen economy. This may be achieved through new nanostructured materials as electrical catalysts. An ideal source, therefore, would be to use solar power to produce hydrogen by electrolysis of water.

The key to developing hydrogen as an alternative energy carrier is the development of a suitable hydrogen storage nanomaterial. Hydrogen has to be stored at high pressure since although one gram of hydrogen gas will drive a car about 100 meters and occupies almost 11 litres (2.9 gallons) of volume at room temperature and atmospheric pressure. In order to match today's cars' average reach of 400-500 kilo-metres per tank filling, 4 to 5 kg, or 40,000 to 50,000 litres, of hydrogen would need to be stored. This is only possible if the gas is stored at a pressure at several hundred atmospheres or under cryogenic temperatures (minus 253 degrees centigrade) to store it in liquid form. Both alternatives have drawbacks. Nanotechnology could be used to encapsulate hydrogen inside hollow molecules, under room temperature. Fullerenes (hydrogen-C60 composites) are ideal nanocages for this purpose, not only because they are hollow but also because hydrogen can be adsorbed on the fullerene surface. This process is currently the subject of intense research (19).

Nanostructures have a much larger surface area than bulk materials, so they could hold more hydrogen per unit weight. One technique involves storing hydrogen in a solid form as a metal hydride compound. Metal hydride nanostructures could greatly improve the efficiency of this type of storage. Finding the optimum conditions for fabricating metal hydride nanostructures to achieve highly efficient hydrogen storage has to be researched.

Hydrogen Fuel Cells

Nanotechnology is also moving hydrogen fuel cell research and development forward. It holds the potential to put hydrogen storage directly in the fuel cell using nanoengineered carbon, zeolites or stacked clays and the potential to reduce vehicular emissions.

Nanoengineered electrodes in the form of cathodes and anodes are currently being manufactured and incorporated in solid oxide and polymer electrode-based fuel cells. These provide higher efficiency and performance with increased surface area and lower volume, as well as improving the functioning and durability of fuel cells' membranes.

Fuel cells could replace the internal combustion engines in cars and the steam turbines in power stations as the means of turning chemical energy into useful power. Rather than burning carbon-based fuels and therefore releasing carbon dioxide, fuel cells convert the chemical energy of hydrogen directly into electricity, producing only water as a by-product. Since a fuel cell is not subject to the same thermodynamic constraints as a heat engine, it can be made much more efficient than an internal combustion engine. Most leading car manufacturers, including General Motors, Daimler-Chrysler, Ford and Toyota are researching and developing fuel cells.

Electronics companies such as Toshiba and Samsung, as well as smaller start-up companies, are working towards micro-fuel-cell technology to replace the batteries in mobile phones and laptop computers.

Wind Power

Most of the data shown below was taken from a variety of internet sources (20). Wind power is the conversion of wind energy into a useful form, such as electricity, using wind turbines. At the end of 2007, worldwide capacity of wind-powered generators was 94.1 gigawatts. Although wind currently produces about 1% of worldwide electricity use, it accounts for approximately 19% of electricity production in Denmark, 9% in Spain and Portugal, and 6% in Germany. Globally, wind power generation increased more than fivefold between 2000 and 2007.

Historically windmills have been used for centuries as a source of mechanical energy for pumping water or grinding grain. Now they are used to drive turbines to generate electricity. This is done on a small or large scale. The latter are wind farms that supply electricity to the electrical grid.

Wind energy is plentiful, renewable, widely distributed, clean, and reduces greenhouse gas emissions when it displaces fossil-fuel-derived electricity. The intermittency of wind seldom creates problems when using wind power to supply a low proportion of total demand. Where wind is to be used for a moderate fraction of demand, additional costs for compensation of intermittency are considered to be modest.

There are now many thousands of wind turbines operating, with a total capacity of 73,904 MW of which wind power in Europe accounts for 65% (2006). Wind power was the fastest growing energy source at the end of 2004. World wind generation capacity more than quadrupled between 2000 and 2006. 81% of wind power installations are in the US and Europe, but the share of the top five countries in terms of new installations fell from 71% in 2004 to 62% in 2006.

In 2007, the countries with the highest total installed capacity were Germany, the United States, Spain, India, and China (see Table 10.3). By 2010, the World Wind Energy Association expects 160 GW of capacity to be installed worldwide.

Biofuels

There is an extensive background of material, including roadmaps, on the status and future of biofuels available on a number of websites (21), (22), (23), (24). Increasingly in the search for alternative energy sources, fuels can be made from recent dead biological material which distinguishes it from fossil fuels, which are derived from long dead biological material. They can be in the form of solid, liquid, or gas. They offer the possibility of producing energy without a net increase of carbon into the atmosphere because the plants used to produce the fuel have already removed CO_2 from the atmosphere. Biofuel is therefore more nearly carbon neutral and less likely to increase atmospheric concentrations of greenhouse gases.

Biofuels are used globally, most commonly to power vehicles and cooking stoves. New industries have created and are expanding in Europe, Asia and the Americas. Biofuels reduce the dependence on petroleum and is becoming available as a low cost source. For this reason many countries are growing crops high in sugars for the production of ethanol and high in oils to produce biodiesel. These products are now being mixed with conventional petroleum to provide a lower cost fuel for use in motor vehicles. Biofuels from plant materials convert energy that was originally captured from solar energy via photosynthesis. A comparison of conversion efficiency from solar to usable energy shows that photovoltaics are 10 times more efficient than the best biofuel.

Each region of the world has a set of objectives for the development of biofuel as a sustainable resource for their future needs.

The United Nations have expressed concerns that the conversion of crops to producing fuel could seriously affect food supply particularly in countries like Africa that rely on low cost imports. This issue of food production has to feature in any long term plan involving biofuels.

In the US, the current Government has set up an act (25) that requires the country to replace 75% of imported oil by alternative sources of energy including biofuels by 2025. This requires producers to use at least 36 billion gallons of biofuel. This is already reducing food exports and increased grain prices worldwide.

In Europe the European Union (EU) revised its directive on biofuels in 2008 (26) to a value of 20% by the year 2020. The European

Table 10.1: Energy Sources

Sustainable	Current Status
Conservation / Efficiency	- not enough
Hydroelectric	--not enough
Biomass	- not enough
Wind	--not enough
Wave & Tide	--not enough
Geothermal HDR	- not enough
Solar terrestrial	--high cost
Solar power satellites	high cost
Chemical	
Natural Gas	sequestration, high cost
Clean Coal	sequestration, high cost
Hydrogen	to be developed
Nuclear	
Nuclear Fission	practical and used (radioactive waste) issue,
Nuclear Fusion	to be developed?, high cost?

Table 10.2: Summary of Environmentally Beneficial Nanotechnologies

Application	Impact of Nanotech in Area (a)	Infrastructural Changes (b)	Benefit CO_2 per annum (c)	Timescale for implementation (Yrs) (d)
Fuel Efficiency	Critical	Low	<3	<5
Insulation	Moderate	Low	<3	3-8
Photovoltaics	High	Moderate	C6	<5
Electricity Storage	High	High	10-42	10-40
Hydrogen Economy	Critical	Very High	29-120	20-40

(a) Impact of nanotechnology - describes the effect nanotechnology is likely to have in the area compared to other technologies.
(b) Infrastructural change- indicate the effort to bring the nanotechnology to market.
(c) Benefit - estimate of the maximum potential CO^2 saving
(d) Timescale for implementation

(Reference: Environmentally Beneficial Nanotechnologies' from the UK's Department for Environment, Food and Rural Affairs (DEFRA), published in May 2007)

Commission supports 14 biofuel programmes within the European Biofuels Technology Platform (27). These involve technologies and markets studies. One such two year programme, known as REFUEL (28) has a key objective to develop a roadmap for biofuels that enables an effective market penetration by 2030. To help achieve this goal, a biofuels roadmap will be developed that is consistent with EU biofuel policies and supported by stakeholders involved in the field.

Amongst rural populations in developing countries, biomass provides the majority of fuel for heat and cooking, wood and animal dung being materials commonly used. Figures from the International

Table 10.3: Installed Windpower Capacity (MW)

Rank	Nation	2005	2006	2007
1	Germany	18,415	20,622	22,247
2	United States	9,149	11,603	16,818
3	Spain	10,028	11,615	15,145
4	India	4,430	6,270	8,000
5	China	1,260	2,604	6,050
6	Denmark	3,136	3,140	3,129
7	Italy	1,718	2,123	2,726
8	France	757	1,567	2,454
9	United Kingdom	1,332	1,963	2,389
10	Portugal	1,022	1,716	2,150

Energy Agency show that biomass energy provides around 30% of the total primary energy supply in developing countries; over 2 billion people depend on biomass fuels as their primary energy source.

In Asia and the developing countries, biofuel industries are becoming established. India and China are developing both bioethanol and biodiesel programs. The Indian sugar ethanol program sets a target of 5% bioethanol incorporation into transport fuel. China is a major bioethanol producer and aims to incorporate 15% bioethanol into transport fuels by 2010.

The future of biofuels as an alternative source will depend upon a number of factors, technological process development, cost of oil and gas and their continued availability and lower cost alternatives such as hydrogen or solar panels. Breakthrough in biotechnology and genetics could provide lower cost processing. By replacing natural genes in yeast and bacteria for synthetic ones, microbes can produce hydrocarbons—creating billions of microscopic refineries to turn simple sugars into petroleum.

TRANSPORT

Roadmapping future transport systems is one of the greatest challenges for planners and technologists. Efficient and effective transportation is essential for developing the future world. There are three components to consider – modes of transport for land, sea and the air, integration of these modes into a network and the fuel they will need. No significant advances in the design of vehicles, aircraft or ships will be made until new fuels, materials and different methods of locomotion are developed. It is a certainty that automated integrated transport systems will be required to connect cities, countries and even regions so that people and goods can travel unimpeded.

Cars

Many large motor manufacturers have designs for electrically driven vehicles that will run on a mixture of fuels. The so-called hybrid cars are being tested for use in cities. Currently, Toyota's hybrids combine a gas engine with an electric one. Ultimately, hybrids could pave the way for fuel cell cars. In fuel cells, energy is produced from a chemical reaction when a molecule passes through a reactive membrane whereas combustion engines create energy by igniting fuel via flame or heat. All-electric cars that can be charged at home are an attractive option but battery technology has not yet reached a stage where they would be practical or economical for long journeys. Fuel cell cars have already been produced by major manufacturers in the US, Germany and Japan. The world's first fuel cell car was produced and operated in 1998 (28). It is based on a Mercedes A-class compact car and produces its hydrogen fuel onboard from reformation of methanol.

Three key obstacles for fuel cell based vehicles are the cost of the fuel cells, the cost of making the hydrogen, and making fuel cells more powerful and cost-effective. The commercial issues of how hydrogen is safely made, stored and distributed and used in vehicles will have to be resolved before this technology becomes universally accepted. As stated earlier, metal hydrides are being considered as a possible storage medium but they add unacceptable weight to the vehicle. Carbon nanotube structures could be able to store enough hydrogen and are the subject of intense study since they may offer a solution to the weight problem.

If, in our roadmap we look beyond the next two decades, even beyond 2050, what are we likely to see? Transport systems will be very different and individual transport such as cars may be replaced by automated mass transport systems. Remotely controlled taxis or people movers as can be seen in some theme parks, such as Disney World, could be in use.

Flying cars or sky cars could also be another possibility but these would be small aircraft that can take off and land like Gyrocopters, parked on roof tops or alongside houses. There are many different designs and prototype proposals in existence since it has been a dream of aeronautical engineers for decades. Sky cars can take many forms. Basically using conventional drive systems, they would be vertical take-off planes with foldable wings to enable them to be securely stowed away in garages. The real breakthrough that will make sky cars realisable will be new propulsion systems based on electric or electromagnetic powered fuel cells or from a national grid to which the vehicle could connect, similar to what was shown in a recent Star Wars film.

Trains

Japan and Germany have developed train systems based on electromagnetic levitation, known as MAGLEV (Superconducting Magnetically Levitated Vehicle), a super high-speed train with a non-adhesive drive system that is independent of wheel-and-rail frictional forces. MAGLEVs, a combination of superconducting magnets and linear motor technology, are able to realise super high-speed running, safety, reliability, low environmental impact and minimum maintenance.

The operational costs of MAGLEVs are high at present so their use is limited. But cheap electromagnetic propulsion systems could be developed if superconductivity could be realised at normal temperatures. A superconductor is a material that has no resistance to electric current flow below a certain critical temperature. In a closed circuit with a perfect superconductor, current will flow forever. This would mean no energy loss, hence low power costs. Could nanotechnology solve the problem by making new superconducting materials that would operate at room temperature? Most of the chemical compounds used so far only superconduct at liquid gas temperatures which limit their use owing to the practicalities and economics of employing cryogenic systems. Molecular superconductors, including carbon nanotubes, are being studied but at present they also only work at cryogenic temperatures. A single development of such materials would revolutionise transportation. Instead of highways filled with cars, silent, levitated hover-trains would glide around cities and electrically driven personal carriers and walkways would transport people and goods economically anywhere. It would change the design of buildings, cities and make landscapes appear like they have been portrayed in science fiction. But it is now nearer to reality than is generally known.

MAGLEV trains have been in limited operation in Germany, Japan and China. China provides a service to and from Shanghai Pudong Airport. A new 1200 km system is being constructed to run from Beijing to Shanghai. These trains, based on a well-known principle of electromagnetic induction are likely to be the ground transport systems of the future. It is basically the high construction and operating costs which at present prevents their wider use.

Aircraft

Aircraft design will continue to benefit from new developments in propulsion systems and materials. Nanotechnology will have a role to play in the development of materials for body and engine parts and for fuels. Air travel is growing faster than the technology that supports it. It is an example where the technology is being demand-led by the market.

Aircraft capable of carrying larger payloads at lower costs are the goal of most aircraft manufacturers. The recent addition of the European Airbus consortium's A380 to the fleets of the major airlines is the latest example. Emphasis is on economics and speed, although the latter is related to fuel costs. The Concord *faster than sound* aircraft was a great technical success but it did not generate a new genesis of fast aircraft because it became uneconomic with a limited passenger payload and high operational costs. What is the next stage in aviation? Our roadmap needs to look at 'Space Planes' which, with the current technology, are hybrids of conventional winged aircraft and rock-propelled space vehicles. They are sub-orbital machines that can take off, ascend, descend, and land like conventional aircraft, providing true single stage to orbit capability.

Since June 2004, only two craft, the X-15 and SpaceShipOne, have reached space. Neither of these craft was capable of entering orbit unassisted and both began independent flight only after being lifted to high altitude by a carrier aircraft. NASA and Boeing are currently developing unmanned orbital space plane technologies as a low-cost alternative to expendable launch vehicles for satellite launches.

At a milestone event inside a Mojave Desert hangar Richard Branson demonstrated the possibilities of his fledgling commercial space program by unveiling a carrier aircraft designed to launch a passenger-carrying spaceship (29). Known as White Knight Two, it is the world's largest all-carbon-composite aircraft. White Knight Two and SpaceShipOne's successor, dubbed SpaceShipTwo, are being built by a joint venture called The Spaceship Company. White Knight Two is designed to cradle SpaceShipTwo under its wing and release it at an altitude of 50,000 feet. Once separated, SpaceShipTwo will fire its hybrid rocket and climb more than 68 miles (100 kilometers) above Earth. From that height, which marks the internationally recognized boundary of outer space, up to six passengers and two pilots will be able to float weightless for several minutes and see the curving Earth beneath a black sky.

SpaceShipTwo uses a feathered re-entry system, feasible due to the low speed of re-entry — by contrast, space shuttles and other orbital spacecraft re-enter at orbital speeds, closer to 25,000 km/h (16,000 mph), requiring the use of heat shields. It is designed to re-enter the atmosphere at any angle. If successful, this will mark the beginning of commercial space flights. These flights are very expensive and at present are for rich tourists but when new engine designs, improved materials and lower cost fuels become available then space planes will become truly commercial. They will herald a new age in commercial orbital flying.

Space Vehicles and Exploration

NASA, The US National Aeronautics and Space Administration has set up mission directorates and a Strategic Planning Council to create and implement 13 different strategic roadmaps for use in developing its Integrated Space Architecture. These roadmaps identify decision points for investing in new technology and setting mission priorities. They include:

- Broad science and exploration goals, priorities, recommended activities or investigations and a summary of anticipated discoveries and achievements.
- High-level milestones, options and decision points.
- Suggested implementation approaches and missions sets, with options and possible pathways.
- Key dependencies on and relations to other roadmaps.
- Identification of required capabilities, facilities and infrastructure.
- Roadmapping approach

Each of the 13 roadmaps has been developed by a national committee, made up of members from the Government (including NASA), industry, and the academic scientific community. Generic to the plans is the development of a re-useable replacement for the Space Shuttle. By 2030 this new space vehicle would have been in operation for some years along with other commercial designs. At that time a new type of space station will probably be in orbit to accommodate both scientific personnel and tourists. This station will also be needed to construct new space vehicles for deeper space exploration as the existing International Space Station (ISS) is not suitable for this purpose. Space exploration and space tourism will become a commercial business. Roadmapping the future of space travel and exploration is one of the most challenging and exciting endeavours that can be undertaken.

In this century we are likely to see the construction of a space elevator. It would comprise of a long cable or tower extending from the Earth's surface into space with its centre of mass at geostationary Earth orbit (GEO), at an altitude of 35,000 km directly above the equator. Electromagnetic vehicles travelling along the cable could serve as a mass transportation system for moving people, payloads, and power between Earth and space. This concept was highlighted by Arthur C. Clark in 1978 in his book, *The Fountains of Paradise* (30). At that time, the idea was dismissed as there was no technology available that could make the engineering possible. Now in the twenty-first century, developments in nanomaterials, like carbon nanotubes, increase the possibility of making such a project a reality. Robert Cassanova, director of the NASA Institute for Advanced Concepts, stated that 'a space elevator is scientifically sound and technically feasible' (31). A conceptual design has been done by NASA who are now seriously considering space elevators as a mass-transit system in the late twenty-first century or before. It will be a major international undertaking, perhaps surpassing anything that has gone before.

Developments in aerospace will make 'space transits' a reality; they will be able to take people to the space station or fly around the

Earth in hours rather than days. If, as is planned by 2020, a permanent base on the Moon is established; then later, maybe by 2030, travel to Mars could become a reality. Space projects such as these provide the necessary impetus to advance all types of transportation systems. They enable humans to make giant leaps forward, fulfilling the human desires to explore and discover.

The MAGLEV train and concept car shown in Figure 10.2 are real and operational but flying cars and space planes are concepts for the future.

We now want to move back to Earth with our roadmap to look at another sector that is most important for the majority of people.

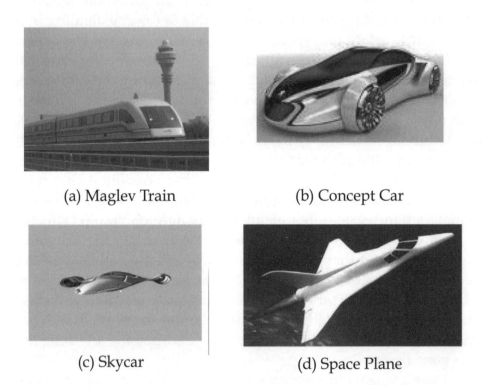

(a) Maglev Train   (b) Concept Car

(c) Skycar   (d) Space Plane

Figure 10.2

THE FUTURE OF MEDICINE AND HEALTH

Any roadmap of the future has to include medicine and health since it is basic to all human need. New knowledge and technologies have opened up unparalleled opportunities and possibilities for medicine and healthcare. The control and eradication of disease, the repair and replacement of organs and generic therapies that one day will improve the quality of life and increase its longevity.

Expenditure on world healthcare is now over US$ 3 trillion and rising which makes it the world's largest industry. The governments of most countries give health and medicine a high priority. With increasing world population and in some countries a larger ageing population, the demand for healthcare is placing impossible burdens on governments. Technological advances in every field of medicine are raising expectations and pushing up demand for services. In democratic countries politicians and governments have to respond positively to this demand to secure support of the people they represent. They are turning increasingly to science and technology for solutions. The areas where the new technologies are most likely to enhance the quality of life will be in the fields of medical diagnostics, drug delivery and customised therapy. The availability of low cost, easy to use, portable devices and measurement systems will empower people to make their own decisions and plan their own treatment schedules.

The (IFAF) Institute for Alternative Futures (32) sees in the next 25 years the development of a Health Advocate Avatar. This is a knowledge interface that can mediate interactions between individuals and medical knowledge. It would provide an information platform for organizing and integrating personal medical information to the newest advances in biomedical developments, thus enabling individuals to make informed choices about their own healthcare. It is predicted that before 2030 this will become an accepted practice, making healthcare fully personalised.

In the next decade medical practitioners and health specialists will have enough data on genetics and proteomics from patients' records to replace diagnostics with prognostic systems. The mapping of an individual's DNA and linking that knowledge to their health profile will determine their vulnerability to a wide range of diseases. This will advance predictive medicine and will enable drugs to be targeted to an individual's specific needs. Wearable computers will record and analyze data from body monitors containing biomarkers that track disease in people at risk. These computers can be securely connected to health monitoring centres. In this way the human population would contribute data directly to a central database for storage and analysis. Clinical diagnosis can be then be validated by accessing a central library of biomarkers thus identifying disease or its early onset.

The continuing development of imaging systems permits visualisation of internal organs and body processes, including brain functions. Within the next two decades this will advance our understanding of the relationship between body and mind and lead to a 'predict and prevent' approach to medicine. Eventually these health measures will result in life extension. Antioxidant and hormone replacement therapies will further aid reduction of the ageing process. Future markets will be shaped by anti-ageing and health-enhancement products. Longevity medicine will become an established practice.

It is estimated that within the next two decades human life expectancy for healthy people could approach one hundred years. This means that many people reading this book who avoid a life-threatening disease will see the twenty-second century. Longevity medicine will retard the ageing process and promote better health and quality of life; but it will also have profound political, economic and cultural consequences for society. Here we can see how bio-nanotechnology through advances in medicine and medical practice will change society beyond anything that has gone before. This leads us to the field of nanomedicine.

Nanomedicine
Biomedicine and biology are currently undergoing an information revolution. Huge amounts of data are being generated from DNA

sequencing, molecular structures and macromolecular structures (proteins, RNA, DNA); and from modelling and visualizing biological pathways (metabolic, signalling, genetic control).

Nanomedicine is a sub-set of biomedicine. It can be loosely defined as the preservation and improvement of human health using molecular tools and knowledge of the human body's biochemistry. Nano-sized tools are used for the diagnosis, prevention and treatment of disease. They help to gain increased understanding of the complex underlying physiology of disease. Nanomedicine will shape the future direction of medicine.

In 2005, the European Science Foundation produced a report looking at the future of nanomedicine (33) to identify Europe's strengths and weaknesses. The work for this foresight study report was carried out by a group of 35 experts from academia and industry at workshops held in Amsterdam in 2004. One of the main conclusions was the urgent need to raise awareness and improve communication of the economic and social benefits of nanomedicine to stakeholders and to the wider public. There has to be an acceptance by society that these new technologies have an important role to play. Ignorance breeds fear and misconception, problems that have beset nanotechnology during the last decade.

Current Developments

According to the findings of the IFAF 2029 Project, work is in progress in the following six areas as outlined on their website (34). These will provide the foundations for the future of nanomedicine.

Anti-microbial Properties

An investigation is being carried out on nanomaterials with strong anti-microbial properties such as nanocrystalline silver. This is already being used for wound treatment by coating bandages by some medical centres.

Biopharmaceutics

Efforts are focused on drug delivery applications using nanomaterial coatings to encapsulate drugs and to serve as functional carriers. Nanomaterial encapsulation could improve the diffusion, degradation, and targeting of a drug.

Implantable Materials

Work is centred on using nanomaterials to repair and replace damaged or diseased tissues. Nanomaterial implant coatings could increase the adhesion, durability, and lifespan of implants, and nanostructure scaffolds could provide a framework for improved tissue regeneration. Prosthetic titanium hips and other bones will be replaced with new bones grown from the patient's own stem cells.

Implantable Devices

Efforts are concentrated on implanting small devices to serve as sensors, fluid injection systems, drug dispensers, pumps and reservoirs, and aids to restore vision and hearing functions. Devices with nanoscale components could monitor environmental conditions, detect specific properties, and deliver appropriate physical, chemical, or pharmaceutical responses. In the longer term, the development of nanoelectronic systems that can detect and process information could lead to nanodevices that serve as retina implants by acting as photoreceptors, and cochlear implants by improving nerve stimulation.

Diagnostic Tools

Lab-on-a-chip devices are being used to perform DNA analysis and drug discovery research by reducing the required sample sizes and accelerating the chemical reaction process. Devices could promote early detection and diagnosis of disease. Research is in progress using nanoscale devices and materials to learn more about how biological systems self-assemble, self-regulate, and self-destroy at the molecular level. The following companies, Wyeth and Merck, Pfizer, GSK, Astra Zeneca and Genentech are using nanotechnologies for drug formulation and drug screening employing the technique of quantum dot analysis (35).

Molecular Imaging Systems
Advances in nanomedicine will depend on developments in molecular imaging systems. Molecular imaging is the non-invasive visualization in space and time of normal as well as abnormal cellular processes at a molecular or genetic level of function. It is used to provide characterization and measurement of biological processes in humans (in vivo).

Current non-invasive imaging developments fall into three categories:

Radionuclide Imaging Devices visualize very low concentrations of radionuclide probes in real time and provide quantitative information, but with low image resolution. They can be used for whole body imaging.

a) The PET (Positron Emission Tomography) scan visualizes probes labelled with positron emitting radioisotopes; it is increasingly popular for both research and clinical medicine. It can reveal the presence of lymphoma cancer cells in specific areas of the body earlier and more accurately than previous diagnostic methods.

b) The SPECT (Single Photon Emission Computed Tomography). This uses probes labelled with radioactive isotopes, which emit gamma rays detected by a gamma camera to create the scan.

c) Quantitative Autoradiography is a technique used in the laboratory to visualise radioactively labelled molecules in substances.

d) Radionucleotide Imaging combined with a computed tomography.

(CT) or a nuclear resonance imaging (NRI) scan provides high anatomic definition along with functional imaging for precise location of the selected molecular activity.

<u>*Magnetic Resonance Imaging (MRI)*</u> uses paramagnetic-labelled probes and produces high imaging resolution, but a large concentration of

the probe must be given which can overwhelm the system being investigated.

Optical Imaging uses fluorescent and bioluminescent probes that emit radiation in the visible or near-infrared wavelengths, which can be scanned by optical cameras. Since light can travel only a few millimetres through tissue, it is limited to skin, breast, small animals and endoscopic procedures, not for deep tissues.

Future Developments
In the future, scanners will become so small and inexpensive that they could be used directly by people in their own homes. They will be able to illuminate a large number of biomarkers that identify disease processes. Beyond disease, some experts see that molecular imaging could prove even more important for revealing healthy biological processes as well. Brain scans already show neurological changes that energize areas of the brain associated with human emotions. Molecular markers can be used to highlight other parameters such as stress levels, immune function, balance and energy flow. Molecular imaging will become more important as genomics and proteomics expand the number of relevant molecules to visualize human behaviour.

Stem Cells for the Future (36)
In the coming decades, adult stem cells, if taken from a patient's own body, could hold the key to renewable source of replacement cells and tissues to treat Parkinson's and Alzheimer's diseases, spinal cord injury, stroke, burns, heart disease, diabetes, osteoarthritis, and rheumatoid arthritis.

They could even be used to grow entire organs such as hearts, livers and kidneys. Although much work has to be done, it is likely that the promise of novel cell-based therapies for such pervasive and debilitating diseases will be realised in the near future. One of the hurdles to overcome is to be able to easily and reproducibly manipulate stem cells so that they possess the necessary characteristics for successful differentiation and transplantation.

It is expected that within the coming decade, research will produce a better understanding of how genetic and molecular controls operate within cells such as the signals that turn specific genes on and off to influence the differentiation of the stem cell. This is important in the use of human stem cells to test new drugs.

CONCLUSIONS

At the beginning of this chapter we set out to build our own technology roadmap to the future by looking at where we are now as a starting point for the journey. Results of our research show that technological progress is moving at such a rate that even with access to the latest information from the Internet to capture everything that is currently in progress or planned for the future it is a formidable task. We therefore apologise to our readers for the many areas that have been excluded. By selecting three key sectors, energy supply, transport, medicine and health, we hope the chapter provides a useful and wide enough informative window onto the present and into the future. Moving beyond 2050 becomes speculation since we then enter territory that is both uncharted and uncertain. One hundred years ago it would have been possible to look ahead fifty years with a high degree of success for most science and technology areas. But today, because of the accelerating rate of progress, that cannot be done with any accuracy. Doing so and getting it wrong raises false expectations. Staged roadmapping is a more preferable method. The challenge is to anticipate the problems coming over the horizon; then to have some solutions ready.

Looking at the horizon and what could arise to solve the world's energy supply problems, it is most likely that new technologies will reduce the demand on energy, particularly from fossil fuels. Industry is one of the largest consumers. New manufacturing, recycling processes, better insulating building materials, communities with integrated transport and distribution systems will reshape the energy supply industry. There will be a greater use and dependence on renewable sources such as solar, wind, bio and hydrogen mixed with nuclear. This will reduce dependency on oil and gas, lessen political tension, improve the environment and hopefully by 2050, retard global warming.

There is little doubt that new fuel efficient integrated transport systems will become dominant. The dependence on car ownership will diminish as public systems become more available and less expensive. Revolutionary rail systems like MAGLEV will cut journey times and improve comfort, giving people more work and leisure time in a day. The greatest changes will probably be in air travel, particularly if space planes become a reality. Journey times across the world will be measured in minutes rather than hours.

New transport systems will require billions of investment in the infrastructure to support them. But it will have to be done around the world. This will open up economic opportunities for undeveloped countries and contribute to the formation of a more joined up world.

The huge advances being made in all branches of medicine, surgery, diagnostics, drugs and drug delivery, organ repair and replacement, gene therapies etc. will continue since they are demanded by society. These are already taking healthcare into a new realm. Medicine will transform from being therapeutic to being preventative. This should, but not with certainty, eventually slow down the spiralling healthcare costs. The challenge is to meet people's expectations at costs that are affordable by individuals, governments and the world at large. Longevity medicine awaits us with all the problems it will bring to society. Roadmaps in medicine and healthcare are going to become increasingly important. This is evidenced by the number being produced in the countries of the European Union. But they will only be useful if regularly updated. Today's controversial areas such as stem cell research, cloning, gene therapy, human enhancement and biochip implants will become acceptable practice before 2050.

We are still just wetting our feet in an ocean of knowledge that awaits to be discovered. Building a roadmap to the future is a continuous process, a journey that has no end. But the path is full of exciting possibilities. Some will be from space exploration, the development of new materials with unique properties, others from a better understanding of our planet and life itself. It is a certainty that if we can avoid extinction by any unknown events, then the twenty-first century will be an even greater stepping stone to the future than the last. The authors hope that in a small way this book will help to inform, provoke and stimulate its readers to discover more for themselves and place them in a better position to make a difference.

REFERENCES

1   *Atlas of the Future*, edited by Pearson, I., published by Routledge, 1998.
2   Pearson, I and Lyons, M., *Business 2010-Mapping the New Commercial Landscape,* Pearson, Spiro Press, 7 Aug 2003, ISBN-10: 1844390004.
3   Kurzwell, R., *The Age of Spiritual Machine'*, Viking Penguin, 2004.
4   Kurzwell, R., *The Singularity is Near*, Viking, Penguin, 2005.
5   Canton, J., *The Extreme Future*, published Penguin Books Ltd. Sept 2006.
6   American Society of Mechanical Engineers, ASME report 2028 vision for Mechanical Engineering ,
     http://www.nanowerk.com/news/newsid=6720.php
7   Toffler, A., *Future Shock*, ISBN 0-394-42586-3 (hardcover), Random House, 1970.
8   *Alternate Energy*: assessment and implementation reference book/Winebrake, James J. 2004, The Fairmont Press.
9   *Renewable Energy Technology Roadmap 2020*, European Union publication, http://www.erec-renewables.org/fileadmin/erc_docs/documents/Publications/EREC
10   Bookout, J. Two centuries of Fossil Fuel Energy, Presented at the International Geological Congress, Washington DC July 1985 and published in Episodes, Vol 12 p 257-262 (1989).
11   Norman, P et al., *A New Dawn for Nuclear Power*, Physics World, Vol 20 , No 7
     July 2007.
12   Cartlidge, E., *Bright Outlook for Solar Cells*, Physics World, Vol 20, No.7, July 2007.
13   *Ultra Efficient Photovoltaics*, Technology Review, http://www.technology-review.com
14   King, R. R., et al., *40% efficient metamorphic GaInP/GaInAs/Ge multijunction*

solar cells. Applied Physics Letters 90, 183516 (2007).

15 http://www.futurepundit.com/archives/002789.html
16 Barnham, K.W. J. et al., *Recent results on Quantum well Solar Cells,* Journal of Materials Science in Electronics, Vol 11. No.7., pp. 531-536, October 2000.
17 http://www/nytimes.com/2008/08/15/business/15solar.html
18 Verne, J , *The Mysterious Island,* Book, Wesleyan University Press, Distributed by University Press of New England 2002, first published by 1874, by Hetzel.
19 *Fullerene Nanocages: Capacity for Hydrogen Storage,* Nano Lett, 8 (3) 767-774 , 2008.
20 Wind Ref http:// en.wikipedia.org/wik/wind_power
21 http:// en.wikdedia.org/wiki/Biomass
22 http://ecoworld.com/blog/2006/06/15/solar-power-biofuel-vs-photovoltaics
23 An EU Strategy for Biofuels Commission of the European Communities Brussels, 8.2.2006.
   http://ec.europa.eu/agriculture/biomass/biofuel/com2006_34_en.pdf
24 Biofuels in the European Union, *A Vision for 2030 and Beyond.* A 2006 report that identifies the current situation and future developments,
   http://ec.europa.eu/research/energy/pdf/draft_vision_report_en.pdf
25 2007-12-19 U.S. Energy Independence and Security Act of 2007.
26 The Directive on the Promotion of the use of biofuels and other renewable fuels for transport, officially 2003/30/EC.
   htpp://www.biofuelstp.eu/biofuelsmarkets.html
27 EU Roadmap for biofuels, REFUEL Renewable Fuels for a Sustainable Europe (Altener EIE-05-042).
28 Environmental Science & Technology, Vol 33, Issue 21,pp458 A-462, Nov 1999.
29 http://en.wikipedia.org/wiki/virgin_galactic
30 Arthur C. Clarke; *The Fountains of Paradise,* Published by Ballantine. 1978.
31 http://science.nasa.gov/headlines/y2000/ast07sep_1.htm
32 Institute of Alternative Futures (www.altfutures.com), *The 2029 Project*: *Achieving an Ethical Future for Biomedical R&D,* 2005.
33 European Science Foundation Report, *Scientific Forward Look at Nanomedicine,* February 2005. website: www.esf.org/publication/196/ESPB23.
34 Institute of Alternative Futures (www.altfutures.com), The 2029 Project: *Achieving an Ethical Future for Biomedical R&D*, 2005.
35 Nanotechnology – Product News, Country Doctor, July 19, 2004. Accessed online at http://www.countrydoctor.co.uk/education/
36 Stem Cell Research, http://stemcells.nih.gov/info/basics/

GLOSSARY OF TERMS

Terms

Artifical Intelligence - is the intelligence of machines and the branch of computer science which aims to create it.

Bio-Catalysis - the use of enzymes or whole cell systems for effecting the conversion of readily available, inexpensive starting materials to high value products.

Biofuels - fuel that can be made from recent dead biological material which distinguishes it from fossil fuels, which are derived from long dead biological material.

Bioinformatics - applying principles of information sciences and technologies to make the diverse and complex life sciences data more understandable and useful, providing gene and database mining, DNA profiling.

BioMEMS - Biological MicroElectro Mechanical Systems are MEMS systems with applications for the biological/analytical chemistry market.

Biomimetics - the study relating to the adoption of good designs seen in living beings.

Bionanotechnology - molecular motors, biomaterials, single-molecule manipulation technologies, biochip technologies etc.

Biosensors - bio-based sensing of drugs, effects, efficacy.

Bulk Micromachining - the tailoring of structures by machining a wafer's interior using wet chemical techniques and differential etching rates of different crystallographic planes.

Carbon Nanotubes - tiny tubes about 10,000 times thinner than a human hair and consisting of rolled up sheets of carbon hexagons.

Charge-Coupled Device - a device utilizing a technique in which information is stored and transported by means of packets of minute electrical charges.

Chemical Vapor Deposition - the growth of thin solid films on a substrate as the result of thermochemical vapor-phase reactions.

Combinatorial Chemistry - small molecule new drug libraries; rational drug design.

Creative Destruction - occurs in an industry when a new technology or product paradigm replaces the old. The industry becomes redefined and uses a new technology trajectory. This has occurred in microsystems when MEMS-based accelerometers eclipsed the mini-electro-mechanical systems developed for air-bag exploders in passenger cars.

Colloid and interface science - deals with multi-phase systems in which one or more phases are dispersed in a continuous phase of different composition or state.

Deep Reactive Ion Etching - an etching technique that uses plasma to obtain high-aspect-ratio structures or deep features.

Deoxyribonucleic acid - a nucleic acid that carries genetic information in the cell. DNA consists of two long chains of nucleotides wrapped into a double helix and coupled by hydrogen bonds. The sequence of nucleotides in the DNA determines individual hereditary characteristics. DNA is responsible for all protein synthesis and handling genetic information in living beings.

Delphi questionnaire - based on a structured process for collecting and distilling knowledge from a group of experts by means of a series of questionnaires interspersed with controlled opinion.

Design for Manufacturability - statistical information on manufacturing process characteristics used to ensure that the device design falls within the parameters of normal manufacturing variances for each process element.

Design Rules - rules for design of a device, established by repeated part fabrication, or materials testing, and includes minimum feature widths, minimum feature spacing, feature overlap dimensions, etch release hole spacing, material characteristics, etc.

Discontinuous Innovation - fundamental and far-reaching product changes that require the users or producers to change.

Disruptive Technology - those technologies that have redefined the technology/product paradigm in an existing application area and have created the basis for a new industry.

Drug Delivery Technologies - new methods for drug delivery.

Fab - the informal name for a chip manufacturer's fabrication plant where ICs or MEMS devices are made. SEMICON industry term for a foundry.

Finite-Element Analysis - a simulation procedure for analyzing multiphysics behavior.

Foresight Programme - a Foresight programme is about looking towards, and preparing for the future.

Fuzzy Logic - a method to mathematically represent uncertainty and ambiguity and provide formalized tools to deal with data whose boundaries are not sharply defined (i.e. are fuzzy). Some PalmTops use fuzzy logic to recognize handwriting.

Genomics - includes gene chips, micro arrays, expression analysis.

Global Economy - benefits derived from the global marketing of products and services.

Google – an INTERNET search engine.

High Aspect Ratio Micromachining - micromachining techniques for manufacturing microstructures of aspect ratios.

High-throughput Screening - technologies for candidate assessment and drug or lead discovery.

The Hydrogen Economy - is a proposed method of deriving the energy needed for motive power (cars, boats, airplanes), buildings or portable electronics, by reacting hydrogen with oxygen.

Hydrogen Fuel Cells - convert the chemical energy of hydrogen directly into electricity, producing only water as a by-product.

Ink-jet printers - operate by propelling variably-sized droplets of liquid or molten material (ink) from a micronozzle onto almost any sized page.

Innovation - innovation is the commercial exploitation of new ideas to develop novel products, processes, services or business models.

Integration - bringing parts together to make a unified whole.

Invention - the creation of a new idea or concept.

Interconnection - a series of connections and interconnections are required in moving from the nano-size domain to the macro-size domain where humans communicate with and use products.

MAGLEVs - a combination of superconducting magnets and linear motor technology, is able to realise super high-speed running, safety, reliability, low environmental impact and minimum maintenance.

Manufacturing Technologies - protein production, fermentation, cell culture, molecular farming or access to GMP facilities.

Metabolomics - metabolic profiling, drug effects.

Micro Electro Mechanical System (MEMS) - a term primarily used in the United States for a micro-sized device with both electrical and mechanical functionality.

Microelectronics - this technology includes techniques used to manufacture ICs, discrete microelectronic devices, MEMS devices such as sensors and actuators, and various electro-optic devices.

Micro Electro-Optical Mechanical Systems - MEMS devices that have applications in optical telecommunications. Also known as optical MEMS.

Microfluidics - the science of designing, manufacturing, and formulating devices and processes that deal with nanoliter or pico-liter volumes of fluids, i.e. (10^{-9} or 10^{-12} liters). Microfluidic studies include nozzles, pumps, reservoirs, mixers, valves, etc., that can be used for a variety of applications including drug dispensing, ink-jet printing, and general transport of liquids, gases and, their mixtures.

Microfabrication - a manufacturing technology for making microscopic devices, such as integrated circuits or MEMS.

Micromachines - mechanical devices with microscopic dimensions. This term is preferred in Japan and is used interchangeably with MEMS and MST.

Micromanufacturing - the production of microsystems products using microfabrication, packaging, microassembly, and other technologies associated with microelectronics and microsystems.

Micropackaging - the processes used to make the connections/interconnections, encapsulate, and protect the MEMS/micro device or nano device or subsystem so that it is ready to be microassembled into a product usable in the macro world.

Microsystem - a microscale device that combines some of the following functions: mechanical, optical, chemical, thermal, magnetic, biological, and fluidic, generally integrated with electronics. A microsystem is a packaged assembly where all the connections are in place to interface with the macro world and is usable by the consumer.

MicroSystem Technology (MST) - the term MST is preferred in Europe and Japan in place of MEMS as it the methods and techniques used to fabricate Microsystems.

Microtechnology - technology dealing with matter on the size scale of microns (1millionth of a meter). Microtechnology is a broad term and can refer to microelectronics, MEMS, or any technology that manipulates matter on a micron scale.

Molecular Nanoscience - an emerging interdisciplinary field that combines the study of molecular/ biomolecular systems with the science and technology of nanoscale structures.

Monoclonal Antibodies - human antibodies, vaccines, products.

Moore's Law - the number of transistors the industry would be able to place on a IC chip would double every 18 months. The IC industry has been able to keep pace with this law to date and strives to achieve the same in the future. Named after the co-founder of Intel, Gordon Moore.

Nanocomposites - materials that are created by introducing nanoparticulates into a macroscopic sample material known as a matrix. Part of the growing field of nanotechnology.

Nanomachines- they are biomacromolecules, which are nanoengines acting both as thermal engines and as informational engines like the so- called "assemblers" (cf. Molecular nanotechnology). The latter are not "self- programmed" like nanobiomachines.

Nanomanufacturing - the production of nanosystems products using nanofabrication, packaging, nanoassembly, and other technologies associated with nanoelectronics and nanosystems.

Nanometre - (nm) a unit of measurement equal to one billionth of a metre.

Nanoparticles - both synthetic (bottom-up) and transformative (top-down) fabrication rely on the availability of building-block materials and artifacts such as quantum dots, nanotubes and nanofibers, ultrathin films, and nanocrystals.

Nanosystem - a *nanoscale* device constructed atom by atom that combines or simulates some of the following functions: mechanical, optical, chemical, thermal, magnetic, fluidic, and/or electronics.

Nanotechnology - technology dealing with matter on a molecular-size scale, on the order of nanometres (1 billionth of a metre).

Top-Down Nanosystems - these systems utilize metaphors such as "chip" (large scale integrated nanosystems) or a "cell" (small complex nanosystems that function in larger quantities) that are revolutionary in nature and require a much longer term to develop. They utilize MEMS based manufacturing technologies.

Top-Down Nanotechnology - engineers taking existing devices, such as transistors, and making them smaller using microtechnology techniques.

Pharmacogenomics – applying the power of genomics to the prediction of individual responses to medication.

Photodynamic Technologies - light-activated processes.

Photonics - the science of generating, controlling, and detecting photons, particularly in the visible and near infra-red spectrum.

Powertrain - refers to the group of components that generate power and deliver it to the road surface, water, or air.

Product Roadmaping - links market and competitive strategy to product plans to technology strategy – with quantitative targets and plans for achieving objectives.

Proteomics - studies of protein identity, interactions, 2D gels.

Quantum Encryption - uses quantum mechanics to guarantee secure communication. It enables two parties to produce a shared random bit string known only to them, which can be used as a key to encrypt and decrypt messages.

Reactive Ion Etching - dry etching by plasma having chemically active gas ions.

Robotics - a robot is a manufactured mechanical or virtual agent with a degree of artificial intelligence.

Smart Sensor - the electronics associated with a sensor that processes the output and are partially or completely integrated on a single chip.

Stem Cell Technologies - tissue- and cell-based regeneration.

SWOT Analysis - is a strategic planning method used to evaluate the Strengths, Weaknesses, Opportunities, and Threats involved in a project or in a business.

Sustainable chemistry - aspirates to raise the stake of less dangerous chemicals as well as production of environmentally high-quality products from preferable renewable resources. This obviates emissions and excessive consumption of resources like energy and materials

Technology Roadmapping - roadmapping enables the best path to reach an objective. Roadmaps link strategy to future actions and explicitly incorporate a plan for needed capabilities and technologies to be in place at the right times.

Tissue engineering - is the use of a combination of cells, engineering and materials methods, and suitable biochemical and physiochemical factors to improve or replace biological functions.

Technology/Product Paradigm - the technology a company utilizes to form a "core product" that acts as a platform from which many application-specific products can be developed. It is a matrix describing the relationship between the various technologies and products of a company.

243

Acronyms

AIChE	American Institute of Chemical Engineers
AFM	Atomic Force Microscope
APM	Atomically Precise Manufacturing
BSI	British Standards Institute
CAD	Computer Aided Design
CCD	Charge-Coupled Device
CCLRC	Council for the Central Laboratory of the Research Councils
CEO	Chief Executive Officer
CLEPA	The European Association of Automotive Suppliers
CMOS	Complimentary Metal Oxide Semiconductor
CNID	Centre for Nanoscience Innovation and Defence
CNTS	Carbon Nanotubes
CT	Computed Tomography
CVD	Chemical Vapour Deposition
DARPA	Defence Advanced Research Agency
DFM	Design for Manufacturing
DfMM	Design for Micro-Nano Manufacture
DNA	Deoxyribonucleic Acid
DRAM	Dynamic Random Access Memory
DRIE	Deep Reactive Ion Etching
DTI	UK Department of Trade and Industry
EC	European Commission
ELVs	End-of-Life vehicles
EPSRC	Engineering and Physical Research Council
EU	European Union
ev	Electron Volt

ESF	European Science Foundation
FP	Framework Programme for R&D
GM	Genetically Modified
HASS	High Altitude Aircraft and Airship Sensing
HTT	High Throughput Technology
IBM	International Business Machines
ICT	Information and Communication Technology
IEEE	Institute of Electrical and Electronic Engineers
IEMI	International Electronics Manufacturing Initiative
IMAPS	The International Microelectronics and Packaging Society
IP	Intellectual Property
IR	Infra Red
ISO	International Organization for Standardization
IT	Information Technology
ITRS	International Technology Roadmaps for Semiconductors
KTN	Knowledge Technology Transfer
KWh	Kilowatt-hour
LoC	Lab-on-Chip
MAGLEV	Superconducting Magnetically Levitated Vehicle
MANCEF	Micro and Nanotechnology Commercialisation Education Foundation
MINAM	Micro-Nanomanufacturing
MMC	Micromachine Centre (Japan)
MNT	Micro-nanotechnology

MOEMS	Micro electro-optical mechanical systems
MRI	Magnetic resonance imaging
OECD	Organisation for Economic Co-operation and Development
NASA	National Aeronautics and Space Administration
NBIC	Nanoscience, Biotechnology, Information Technology and Cognitive Science
NEMS	Nano Electro-Mechanical Systems
NEXUS	Network of Excellence in Multifunctional Microsystems
NCN	The UK's National Composite Network
NIH	National Institutes of Health
NIST	National Institute of Standards and the Technology
NNI	National Nanotechnology Initiative
NPL	National Physical Laboratory
NSF	National Science Foundation
NRM	Nanotechnology Roadmap
NSET	Nanoscale Science, Engineering and Technology
PC	Personal Computer
PDT	Photodynamic therapy
PoC	Point-of-Care
PV	Photovoltaic
PVD	Physical Vapour Deposition
RAE	Royal Academy of Engineering
RAM	Random Access Memory
R&D	Research and Development
RIE	Reactive Ion Etching
RF	Radio Frequency

RFID	Radio Frequency Identification Tags
RS	Royal Society
SBIR	Small Business Innovation Research Program
SEMI	Semiconductor Equipment and Materials International
SIA	The Semiconductor Industry Association
SRA	Strategic Research Agenda
SPD	Severe Plastic Deformation
STREEP	Social, Technological, Economic, Environmental and Political
SWOT	Strengths, Weaknesses, Opportunities, and Threats
TW	Terawatt

INDEX